PUBLICATIONS OF THE SCOTTISH COUNCIL FOR
RESEARCH IN EDUCATION

XXXII

TRADITIONAL NUMBER RHYMES
AND GAMES

TRADITIONAL NUMBER RHYMES AND GAMES

By

F. DOREEN GULLEN, M.A., B.Litt.

UNIVERSITY OF LONDON PRESS, Ltd.

WARWICK SQUARE, LONDON, E.C. 4.

1950

Printed in Great Britain by
ROBERT CUNNINGHAM & SONS LTD., Longbank Works, Alva

PREFACE

In the Panel on Early Number Teaching of the Scottish Council for Research in Education Miss Margaret Drummond, who during her lifetime did so much for the advancement of early child psychology and education, remarked that although the repetition of number rhymes by young children did not contribute to a knowledge of number, it created a pleasurable attitude to number. The Panel felt that acquaintance with Scottish number rhymes was fast dying out and that this would be a distinct loss to Scottish culture. They accordingly decided that such rhymes should be assembled and made available to infant teachers.

The task of collecting the rhymes fell to Miss F. Doreen Gullen, Secretarial Assistant to the Council, who, on leaving the Council, readily agreed to complete the undertaking. The Research Council is pleased to have Miss Gullen's name identified with one of its publications.

The thanks of the Council are also due to the students of the Scottish Training Colleges, to many infant mistresses and to others who contributed to the collection, and to Mr and Mrs William Montgomerie to whose notable work in the collection of Scottish rhymes this more specialised collection is deeply indebted.

W. L. McKINLAY
Convener of Panel on
Early Number Teaching

v

COMMITTEE ON PRIMARY SCHOOL SUBJECTS

PANEL ON EARLY NUMBER TEACHING

Convener of the Committee on Primary School Subjects:

W. D. RITCHIE, O.B.E., M.A., F.E.I.S.,   Director of Education for Selkirkshire

Convener of the Panel on Early Number Teaching:

W. L. McKINLAY, M.A., B.Sc., F.R.G.S., F.E.I.S.,   Head Teacher, The Mount Junior Secondary School, Greenock

Panel on Early Number Teaching:

D. KENNEDY-FRASER, M.A., B.Sc., F.R.S.E.
MAY V. D. GREIG, F.E.I.S.
RUBY A. D. MACDONALD, F.E.I.S.
ANNIE C. MACLARTY, M.B.E., J.P., F.E.I.S.
D. MOWATT, M.A., B.Sc., F.S.S.
A. M. ORR, M.A., B.Sc., F.E.I.S.
JESSIE RUNCIMAN, F.E.I.S.
SISTER MARY, S.N.D., M.A., Ed.B.
J. M. THYNE, M.A., Ed.B.

Ex officiis:

R. R. RUSK, M.A., B.A., PH.D.,   Director to the Scottish Council for Research in Education

A. J. BELFORD, J.P., M.A., F.E.I.S.,   Honorary Secretary to the Scottish Council for Research in Education

CONTENTS

INTRODUCTION

WHEN this work was originally planned the Panel on Early Number Teaching had two purposes in mind: to supply teachers with informal number material natural and agreeable to their youngest pupils, and to try to recover for the pupils some of their heritage of Scottish number rhyme which threatens to be lost in the rush and jostle of modern life. It was accordingly proposed to make a collection of the rhymes, songs and games bearing on number practised in school or out of it by pupils and teachers alike. It became clear, however, in the process of compilation, that unless limits were imposed the material would get out of hand. This monograph, then, contains only traditional material. The Appendices indicate where further information or material may be sought. It is in no sense to be regarded as a text book for teaching purposes.

The descriptions of games have been taken mainly from Mrs A. B. Gomme's encyclopaedic collection of *The Traditional Games of England, Scotland and Ireland*, published in 1894.

Even within these limitations it has sometimes proved a delicate matter to decide on the inclusion, or, more heartrending, the exclusion of an item. What is traditional to the child may be copyright to the adult, and children have a fine free way with texts which may be life to poetry but is certainly withering to the writer's self-esteem. The compiler has endeavoured to avoid copyright difficulties by including only material to which, so far as she is aware, no name can be attached, reluctantly giving up many delightful rhymes which ought to be common property and which, in fact, are regarded as such by other collectors with less conscience. But if the compiler's restraint with regard to one or two number rhymes should lead readers to make direct contact with the diverse excellences, for instance, of Christina Rossetti, Eleanor Farjeon or Rose Fyleman, it will have achieved more than plunder could. In the same way the compiler can but recommend teachers to make their own collections of such suitable verses as Keats's 'There was a naughty boy', Marie de L. Welch's 'Baby Linnet' (which can be found in *The Weekend Book*) or Andrew Dodds's 'Stacking' from *Antrin Songs* and other accidental felicities which occur throughout Scottish and English verse. If, in spite of every effort, there has been through ignorance or inadvertence any infringement of proprietary rights, the compiler apologises in advance and promises to make amends and acknowledgment in any later edition, provided she is allowed to retain the loot.

Though children are at the mercy of adults with regard to what is presented for their choice they are the final arbiters of what constitutes suitable material, and their selection is as unpredictable as its range is extensive. They adopt as their own with equal ease pantomimes of old marriage and fertility rites, political lampoons, the proverbial wisdom of their elders and the most puerile nonsense and freely adapt them to their own serious purposes. They are likewise conservative; thus while almost anything will do for a counting-out rhyme, the most favoured are well-worn formulas which bear their ancient origin clearly on their nonsensical faces. At the nursery stage magic is far more than meaning and rhythm than either, and for this reason also a liberal view must be taken of rhyme. This collection includes some material which may not accord with modern conditions, and some, like 'Green cheeses, yellow laces', or 'Currants and raisins a penny a pound' which are obviously out of date, for who knows where the memory may not linger on, or to what use the old rhymes may yet be put?

It does, nevertheless, seem to be true that many rhymes have suffered an eclipse in recent years. Profitable sociological research might be undertaken in school playgrounds into the decline of the old set games with their organisation and songs, and the implications of such a decline. Many of the old nominies, too, have been dropped or streamlined in accordance with modern impatient tendencies.

In view of the fluid nature of oral tradition, and the great diversity of variants, local and temporal, of which it is capable, the compiler has been very glad, wherever possible, to adopt a form already in print, and would here pay grateful tribute to previous collectors in the field who have rendered the work much simpler. It cannot be too clearly emphasised that this is a selection with a special purpose, and not a balanced collection, and that it makes no attempt whatever to supersede its predecessors, but rather to direct attention to them for the sake of the riches they contain and of which it gives but a one-sided sample. Neither does it pretend to be complete. It is intended to serve as a memorandum to the teacher of the material, or the kind of material, which she may expect some of her pupils to bring to school with them; and some of which all her pupils would be the richer for possessing. And if she finds other or better material in her own locality the compiler would be most grateful to be advised of it.

The classification of the rhymes is admittedly somewhat arbitrary. The *Finger and Toe Counts and Games* are in one or two instances so juvenile as to be pre-school, almost pre-nursery-school. This section might have been enlarged by enumerations of other parts of the body, as, for example, 'Brow brinky', 'Knock at the Door', and so on, but it was felt that these did not lead on to number concepts in the same way as the finger-and-toe counts.

The variety and the combinations and recombinations, found in *Counting-Out Rhymes*, rendered it impossible to give more than a selection, but an effort has been made to make the selection representative.

It seems probable that a child develops a clearer number sense from these rhythmical and symbolical enumerations than he does at first from those rhymes in which numbers are mentioned by name. In many of the latter the occurrence of a number name is equivalent to the appearance of nine bean rows on Yeats's 'Innisfree'—it fits the rhyme. Nevertheless, examples are given particularly where the verse is short enough to make each word memorable, for the sake of accustoming the ear and the tongue to the sound if not the mind to the concept. Cardinals, ordinals, distribution without summation (three—'One for me and one for you, and one for sister Mandy'—'Hippety hop to the barber's shop'), and relative vocabulary (as, 'two', 'both', 'a pair', 'one' and 'another') have been included without distinction in the section *Vocabulary of Number*.

Almost any rhyme at all qualifies for entry into the section *Indefinite Quantities* so that favourites can easily be introduced here.

The compiler is regretfully aware of the inadequacy of the section on *Ball-Bouncing*, while 'Skipping Rhymes' are barely touched upon. It is to be hoped that unsatisfied readers will prosecute inquiries in their own neighbourhood, and if the results are rewarding, make them available to their colleagues.

Under *Festivals* have been grouped not only references to the day or season, but also songs or rhymes particular to the festival.

Riddles appear to be more distinctively Scottish than English, and in fact continue to be composed in some parts of Scotland much on the lines of the examples given here. The writer in 1946 for example heard the following in Shetland: 'Tink tank under a bank, Ten about four', the answer to which was 'a cow being milked'. And following this native tradition the late William Soutar composed *One Hundred Riddles in Scots** which may contain suggestions for those wishing to extend their acquaintance with this aspect. Guessing the answer may be well beyond children, but the definitions give all the pleasure of superior knowledge and mystery.

This suggests one final word on the range of content in these rhymes. Many of them, particularly the games, have been those of older children, and indeed of adults, in the past; but they are included here because children learn from their elders, and may be educing their own kind of enjoyment from quite incomprehensible words long before they can make them their own. There is nothing in tradition against the adaptation of any rhyme to suit the circumstances or the performers (and it is to be noted that most of these rhymes lend themselves admirably to action): nor, it is to be hoped, is there anything against the use of rhymes as far up the school as they are enjoyed.

* Edinburgh: The Moray Press, 1937.

FINGER AND TOE COUNTS AND GAMES

I

A finger play beginning with the little finger, in which each finger is shaken rapidly in turn

Dance, my wee man, ringman, midman, foreman,
Dance, dance, for thoomiken canna weel dance his lane.

cf. the English variants—'Dance, Thumbkin, dance' and 'Thumbkin says, "I'll dance" '.

2

A rhyme for working the feet as the child sits on the holder's lap

'Feetikin, feetikin,
  When will ye gang?'
'When the nichts turn short,
  And the days turn lang,
I'll toddle and gang, toddle and gang!'

cf. English rhymes for the same purpose—'Leg over leg', and 'Seesaw, Sacradown'.

3

Here are the lady's knives and forks,
Here is the lady's table;
Here is the lady's looking-glass,
And here's the baby's cradle.

For the first line the fingers are interlaced and the palms of the hands are turned upward; for the second line the palms are turned downward and brought as close together as the interlaced fingers will permit; for the third the index fingers are raised from this position and placed tip to tip; and for the fourth the little fingers are also raised and the hands are rocked.

4

Here's the church, and here's the people;
Here's the door, and here's the steeple;
Here's the pulpit, here are the stairs;
And there's the minister saying his prayers.

5

5

'John Smith, fallow fine,
Can you shoe this horse o' mine?'
'Yes, sir, and that I can,
As weel as ony man!
There's a nail upon the tae,
To gar the pony speel the brae;
There's a nail upon the heel,
To gar the pony pace weel;
There's a nail, and there's a brod,
There's a horsie weel shod.'

The bare foot is patted in accordance with the words of the rhyme.
In some districts the rhyme is used for bouncing a ball.

6

A toe-counting rhyme

'Let us go to the wood,' said this pig;
'What to do there?' says that pig;
'To look for my mother,' says this pig;
'What to do with her?' says that pig;
'Kiss her to death,' says this pig.

7

A clapping game

My mother said that if I should
Play with the gipsies in the wood,
She would say, 'You naughty girl!
You naughty girl to disobey!'

Two children alternately clap their own and each other's hands,
the pace increasing as the rhyme proceeds.

Another version is as follows

My mother said that I never should
Play with the gipsies in the wood;
The wood was dark; the grass was green;
In came Sally with a tambourine.

I went to the sea—no ship to get across;
I paid ten shillings for a blind white horse;
I up on his back and was off in a crack,
Sally, tell my Mother I shall never come back.

8

A foot-patting rhyme

Pitty, Patty, Polt,
Shoe the wild colt;
Here a nail,
There a nail,
Pitty, Patty, Polt.

cf.

Shoe the colt, shoe!
Shoe the wild mare;
Put a sack on her back,
See if she'll bear.
If she'll bear,
We'll give her some grains;
If she won't bear,
We'll dash out her brains!

and

Shoe the colt,
And shoe the mare;
But let the little
Colt go bare!

9

Put your finger in the corbie's hole,
The corbie's no at hame;
The corbie's at the back-door,
Pykin' at a bane.

The English form begins 'Put your finger in Foxy's hole'.

10

An arm- and leg-wagging rhyme

The doggies gaed to the mill,
    This way and that way;
They took a lick out o' this wife's poke,
And a lick out o' that wife's poke,
And a loup in the lead, and a dip in the dam,
And gaed hame walloping, walloping, walloping.

B

11

A finger-count beginning with the thumbs

> This is the man that brak the barn,
> This is the man that stealt the corn,
> This is the man that ran awa',
> This is the man that tell't a',
> And puir Pirly Winkie paid for a',
> paid for a'. (*ad lib.*)

12

> This is Willie Walker, and that's Tam Sim,
> He ca'd him to a feast, and he ca'd him;
> And he sticket him wi' the spit, and he sticket him,
> And he owre him, and he owre him,
> And he owre him, and he owre him,
> Till day brak. (*ad lib.*)

Willie Walker and Tam Sim are the two feet, held at the ankles as the child sits on the holder's lap, and made to go rapidly up and down and over each other in accordance with the words.

13

A finger-count

> This little cow eats grass,
> This little cow eats hay,
> This little cow runs away,
> This little cow does nothing
> But just lie still all day.
> We'll whip her!

14

> This little pig went to market;
> This little pig stayed at home,
> This little pig had roast beef for dinner,
> This little pig had none,
> And this little pig cried
> 'wee-wee-wee' all the way home.

15

A toe-count

> This pig went to the barn,
> This ate all the corn,
> This said he would tell,
> This said he wasn't well,
> This went week! week! week! over the door sill.

16

A finger-count

> Thumb bold,
> Thibity-thold,
> Langman,
> Lickpan,
> Mamma's little man.

17

A finger-count beginning with the thumb

> Thumbkin brak the barn,
> Lickpot stealt the corn,
> Langman carried it awa',
> Berrybarn stood and saw,
> Wee Pirly Winkie paid for a'.

cf.

> This is the man that brak the barn,
>   (p. 8, No. 11.)

18

A finger-play

Two little dicky-birds
Sat upon a wall
One called Peter
The other called Paul.
Fly away, Peter!
Fly away, Paul!
Come back, Peter!
Come back, Paul!

The two index fingers represent Peter and Paul and are made to disappear and re-appear accordingly.

cf.

There were two blackbirds
Sitting on a hill,
The one named Jack,
The other named Jill,
Fly away, Jack!
Fly away, Jill!
Come again, Jack!
Come again, Jill!

These blackbirds may have been relatives of the 'Two little grey birds' which 'sat on a stone' in *Mother Goose*.

TALLIES

19

A duck
And a drake
And a halfpenny cake
And a penny to pay the old baker,
A hop and a scotch is another notch,
Slitherum, slatherum, take her.

This is the rhyme for the game of 'Ducks and Drakes', played by
skimming stones through water. Each line represents one leap of
the stone out of the water.

20

A button-count

A laird, a lord,
A rich man, a thief,
A tailor, a drummer,
A stealer o' beef.

21

A rhyme for counting rings on a top

A lord, a laird, a lily, a leaf,
A piper, a drummer, a hangman, a thief.

COUNTING-OUT RHYMES

ALMOST any set of words will serve as a counting-out device so long as it is a generally accepted formula, and one which will maintain uncertainty till the last possible moment. But a young child's vocabulary consists almost entirely of attempts at definiteness rather than at mystery, and mere nonsense—the babble with which a child puts itself to sleep—will not be accepted by the group. Where, then, are these two requirements to be found? A closer examination of some of the counting-out rhymes given below, in all their phonetic variations may suggest to the reader that the children—from what rigmarole used by a busy mother to keep her baby amused, or from what overheard adult business, who shall say?—have kept echoes of a much older tune in their present play. *The Scottish National Dictionary* gives the following as 'possibly corrupt forms of the numerals used by the shepherds in the hill districts of the old Cymric kingdom of Strathclyde':

> Zeendi, teendi, taedheri, mundheri, baombe,
> hecturi, zecturi, aover, daover, dek.

Sheep-counts still in use in Lincolnshire—

> Yan tan tethera pethera pimp
> Sethera lethera hovera covera dik
> Yanadik tanadik tetheradik petheradik bumpit
> Yanabumpit tanabumpit tetherabumpit petherabumpit figgit

and in Sussex

> One-erum, two-erum,
> Cockerum, shu-erum,
> Shetherum, shatherum,
> Wineberry, wagtail,
> Tarrydiddle, den

also help to throw light on the source of the children's mysteries. J. R. Morrison of Aberdeen Training College points out that the Welsh cardinals have a certain resemblance to words occurring in some of the rhymes—un, dau (feminine, dwy), tri (feminine, tair), pedwar (feminine pedair), pump, chwech, saith, wyth, naw, dêg, un ar ddeg, dauddeg, tri ar ddeg, pedwar ar ddeg, bumtheg, un ar bumtheg, dau ar bumtheg, tri ar bumtheg, pedwar ar bumtheg, ugain (or hugain)—but adds that figgit suggests rather Gaelic fichead, the equivalent of Latin viginti.

22

Around the house, arickity-rary,
I hope ye'll meet the green canary:
You say ay—I say no,
Hold fast—let go!

23

As I gaed up the apple tree
A' the apples fell on me;
Bake a puddin', bake a pie,
Send it up to John Mackay.
John Mackay is no in,
Send it up to the man i' the mune;
The man i' the mune's mendin' his shoon,
Three bawbees and a farden in.

24

As I went up Hicty-picty hill
I met two frichty-picty children.
They asked me this and they asked me that,
And they asked me the colour of my best Sunday hat.
    (*Green, etc.*)   G.R.E.E.N spells green
And O.U.T spells out.

A similar rhyme from Ayrshire runs
    As I went owre the Muckle Brig
    I saw a scabby rat.
    You one it, you two it, you three it, you four it,
    You five it, you six it, you seven it, you *ate* it.

The one who ate it is "het".

This seems to contain a reminiscence of the riddle
        As I gaed owre Bottle-brig,
        Bottle-brig brak;
        Though ye guess a' day
        Ye winna guess that!

The answer to this is *the ice*. Possibly this is a Lanarkshire reference to Bothwell Bridge in that county.

25

As I went up the Brandy hill,
I met my father, wi' gude will;
He had jewels, he had rings,
He had mony braw things;
He'd a cat and nine tails,
He'd a hammer wantin' nails.
Up Jock, down Tam,
Blaw the bellows, auld man,
The auld man took a dance,
First to London, then to France.

26

Eenity, feenity, fickety, feg,
El, del, domen, egg,
Irky, birky, story, rock,
Ann, Dan, Toosh, Jock.
Tak a mell an knock him ower,
Een, twa, three, fower.

27

Eeny, meeny, miny, man,
Erracle, terracle, tiny tan,
One, two, three,
Out goes she.

28

Eeny, meeny, miny, mo,
Catch a nigger by his toe,
When he squeals let him go,
Eeny, meeny, miny, mo.
O - U - T spells out.

29

Eerie, orie, ickery, am,
Pick ma nick, and slick ma slam.
Oram, scoram, pick ma noram,
Shee, show, sham, shutter,
You — are — out.

30

Eetle ottle,
Black bottle,
Eetle ottle,
Out!
If you had been where I have been
You wouldn't have been put out.

31

Elder, belder, limber, lock,
Three wives in a clock,
Sit and sing, and call a spring,
O - U - T spells out.

cf.

Intery, mintery, cutery corn,
Apple seed and apple thorn,
Wire, brier, limber-lock,
Three geese in a flock;
One flew east, and one flew west,
And one flew over the cuckoo's nest.

32

Eseentse teemste tinnery nunnery,
  Hallelujah hallabalum,
I saw the king of the hazle pazle
  Jumping over Jerusalem dyke
Playing on his pee wee pipe.

33

Hickery, dickery, six and seven,
Alabone, crackabone, ten and eleven.
Spin, span, muskidan,
Twiddlum, twaddlum, twenty-one,
O - U - T spells out.

This rhyme, or a variant, was the one which Pet Marjorie, if she
ever met him, is said to have tried to teach Sir Walter Scott. cf.
'Anery, twaery' . . . (p. 17, No. 39).

A debased version of this appears to be contained in

Ingry oory, accry davy,
Ivry cock, splenny lavy,
Fleem flam
Musky dam
Tweedalum, twaddlum, twenty wan,
Black fish, white troot,
Eery orry, you're oot.

34

Hiddlety, diddlety, dumpty,
The cat ran up the plum tree;
Half a crown to fetch her down,
Hiddlety, diddlety, dumpty.

35

Inty, tinty, tethery, methery,
Bank for over, dover, ding,
Aut, taut, toosh;
Up the Causey, down the Cross,
There stands a bonnie white horse:
It can gallop, it can trot,
It can carry the mustard pot.
One, two, three, out goes she!

36

Lemons and oranges, two for a penny:
I'm a good scholar that counts so many;
The rose is red, the leaves are green,
The days are past that I have seen.

37

Master Monday, how's your wife?
Very sick, and like to die.
Can she eat? O yes,
As much as I can buy.
She makes the porridge very thin,
A pound of butter she puts in,
Black puddin', white clout,
Eerie, orie, you are out!

38

Mistress Mason broke a basin,
How much will it be?
Half-a-crown. Lay it down.
Out goes she!

39

One-ery, two-ery, tickery, seven,
Alibi, crackaby, ten and eleven;
Pin, pan, musky dan;
Tweedle-um, twoddle-um, twenty-one;
Eerie, orrie, ourie. You are out!

cf.

Anery, twaery, duckery, seven,
Alama, crack, ten and eleven;
Peem, pom, it must be done,
Come teetle, come total, come twenty-one.

or

One-ery, two-ery, tickery, ten,
Bobs of vinegar, gentlemen;
A bird in the air, a fish in the sea;
A bonnie wee lassie come singing to thee.
One, two, three!

40

Paddy on the railway
Picking up stones,
By came an engine
And broke Paddy's bones.
'Oh', said Paddy, 'that's not fair.'
'Well,' said the engine-driver, 'you shouldn't
be there.'

An older user of this rhyme protests that it was the engine that spoke. 'Paddy' refers to the great number of Irish labourers who came over last century to Scotland to be employed in the making of the railways.

41

Red, white, yellow, blue,
All out but you.

42

Tit-tat-toe!
My first go,
Three jolly butcher boys
All in a row;
Stick one up,
Stick one down,
Stick one in the old man's crown.

This rhyme appears to have been taken over as a counting-out rhyme from its original use in a pencil and paper game described by Gomme.

43

Zeenty, teenty, feggerie fell,
Pompaleerie jig.
Every man who has no hair
Generally wears a wig.

Another version from Ayrshire

Zeenty, peenty, figgery fell,
Ell, ell, dominell,
Zurty purty, tarry rope,
Zan tan, tousy Jock,
Eerie-orie, eerie-orie,
You - are - out.

44

Zeenty, teenty, halligo lum,
Pitchin' tawties doun the lum.
Wha's there? Johnny Blair.
What d'ye want? A bottle o' beer.
Where's your money? In my purse.
Where's your purse? In my pocket.
Where's your pocket? I forgot it.
Go down the stair, you silly blockhead.
You - are - out.

Who was Johnny Blair? He occurs also on p. 50, No. 137.

COUNTING FRUIT STONES

Fortune-telling count

45
He loves me, he loves me not . . .

46
This year, next year,
Sometime, never.

The first fortune-telling count, used in counting fruit-stones or in ball-bouncing, etc., in response to the question, 'When shall I marry?'

Subsequent questions and counts are:

What is the first letter of my husband's name? A, B, C, etc.

What is he? Tinker, tailor, soldier, sailor, rich man, poor man, beggar man, thief.

On what day shall I be married? Monday, Tuesday, Wednesday, etc.

What shall I wear? Silk, satin, cotton, rags.

How shall I get it? Stolen, borrowed, bought or given.

How shall I go to church? Coach, carriage, wheelbarrow, dung-cart.

Where shall I live? Big house, little house, pig stye, barn.

How many children shall I have? One, two, three, etc.

BALL-BOUNCING

47

Game, game, ba', ba',
Twenty lasses in a raw,
No' a lad among them a',
Game, game, ba', ba'.

48

Jenny Wren
Stole a hen,
Dinna let her mammy ken.

The ball is bounced on each accented syllable and the number of
rounds to be achieved without a break-down is stated before the
bouncer begins.

49

Little wee laddie, foo's yer daidie?
New come oot o' a basket shadie.
A basket shadie's ower full,
New come oot o' a roarin' bull.
A roarin' bull's ower fat,
New come oot o' a gentleman's hat.
A gentleman's hat's ower fine,
New come oot o' a bottle o' wine.
A bottle o' wine is ower reid,
New come oot o' a crust o' breid.
A crust o' breid is ower broon,
New come oot o' a half-a-croon.
A half-a-croon is ower little,
New come oot o' a weaver's shuttle.
A weaver's shuttle's ower holey,
New come oot o' a paint pottie.
Game, game, game, game, game!

INDUCEMENT TO COUNT

50

A long-tailed pig, or a short-tailed pig,
Or a pig without a tail;
A sow pig, or a boar pig,
Or a pig with a curly tail.

51

Round and round the rugged rock
The ragged rascal ran.
If you can tell me how many Rs are in *that*
You're a very clever man.

52

The merle and the blackbird,
The laverock and the lark,
The gouldy and the gowdspink,
How many birds be that?

The laverock and the lark,
The baukie and the bat,
The heather-bleet, the mire-snipe,
How many birds be that?

Answer: Three in the first and two in the second verse. (The bat is not a bird.)

53

Thomas a Tattamus took two Ts
To tie two tups to two tall trees,
To frighten the terrible Thomas a Tattamus!
Tell me how many Ts there are in all *that*?

SEQUENCE

54

A, B, buff,
Tak the master a cuff;
Hit him ane, hit him twa,
Ding him to the stane wa'.

55

Divination by magpies

Ane's joy, twa's grief,
Three's a waddin', four's a death,
Five's a coffin, six a hearse,
Seven a great man in distress.

cf.

One's sorrow, two's mirth;
Three's a wedding, four's death;
Five a blessing, six hell;
Seven the deil's ain sel'!

An Irish variant is as follows

One for sorrow,
Two for joy,
Three for a wedding,
Four for a boy,
Five for silver,
Six for gold,
Seven for a secret
That is never to be told.

56

One for anger, two for mirth,
Three for a wedding, four for a birth,
Five for rich, six for poor,
Seven for a witch—
I can tell you no more.

57

A rhyme said when the speaker is anxious to get more of some delicacy

Ane's nane,
Twa's some,
Three's a pickle,
Four's a curn,
Five's a horse-lade,
Six'll gar his back bow,
Seven'll vex his breath,
Aucht'll bear him to the grund,
And nine'll be his death.

cf.

One's none,
Two's some,
Three's a many,
Four's a penny,
Five's a little hundred.

A West Lothian variant is as follows

Ane's alane,
Twa's some,
Three's a pickle,
Four's a pun,
Five's denty,
Six's plenty,
Seven's a horse's laden.

58

Ane, twa,
Fower, five,
Six, seven,
Fisher doddies
Tint their coddies
Comin up
The stane roadies.

59

Ane, twa, three,
My craw's free.

One boy is selected to be craw. He sits down upon the ground,
and he and another boy then hold the two ends of a long strap or

c

twisted handkerchief. The latter also takes into his right hand another hard-twisted handkerchief, called the cout, and runs round the craw, and with the cout defends him against the attacks of the other boys, who, with similar couts, use all their agility to get a slap at the craw. But, before beginning, the guard of the craw must cry out the rhyme given above. The first whom he strikes becomes craw, the former craw then taking the place of the guard. If he wishes respite he must cry:

> Ane, twa, three,
> My craw's no free.

60

> Ane, twa, three,
> Fat a fishers I see,
> Gaein' ower the brig o' Dee,
> Deil pick their muckle greethy ee.

61

> Ane! Twa! Three!
> Ane! Twa! Three!
> Sic a lot o' fisher-wifies
> I do see!

62

> A pye sate on a pear-tree,
> A pye sate on a pear-tree,
> A pye sate on a pear-tree,
> Heigh O! heigh O! heigh O!

> Once so merrily hopp'd she,
> Twice so merrily hopp'd she,
> Thrice so merrily hopp'd she,
> Heigh O! heigh O! heigh O!

63

> Children can hop on one leg,
> Children can walk on two;
> No one walks on three legs,
> But pussies walk on four.

64

Clash-pyotie, clash-pyotie,
Sits on the tree,
Dings doon aipples,
Ane twa three.

Ane tae the maister,
And ane tae the man,
And ane tae the laddie
That cas the caravan.

But nane tae the clash-pyot,
What will we gie,
Gie tae the clash-pyot
That sits on the tree?

A barrow fu' o' muck,
And a barrow fu' o' hay,
And we'll cairry the clash-pyotie
Doon tae the Bay!

65

Glasgow ships come sailing in,
Come sailing in, come sailing in:
Glasgow ships come sailing in
On a fine summer morning.

You daurna set your fit upon,
Your fit upon, your fit upon:
You daurna set your fit upon,
Or Gentle John will kiss you.

Three times will kiss you;
Four times will bless you;
Five times butter and bread
Upon a silver salver.

Who shall we send it to?
Send it to, send it to;
Who shall we send it to?
To Mrs (——)'s daughter.

Take her by the lily-white hand,
Lead her o'er the water;
Give her kisses, one, two, three,
 She's the favourite daughter.

Braw news is come to town,
Braw news is carried;
Braw news is come to town,
(———— ——)'s married.

First she got the kail pot,
Syne she got the ladle;
Syne she got a dainty wean,
 And syne she got a cradle.

All join hands in a circle and move round singing the verses.
The girl named turns her back to the centre of the ring and the
game is resumed. When all in like manner have been named and
have turned, the 'soo's race' ensues; a hurry-scurry round—which
continues until someone falls, and the game ends by all tumbling in
a confused heap.

66

A round or canon

Great Tom is cast,
And Christchurch bells go
One, two, three, four, five, six,
And Tom comes last.

67

Have you any bread and wine,
Bread and wine, bread and wine;
Have you any bread and wine,
 My theerie and my thorie?

Yes, we have some bread and wine, etc.

We shall have one glass of it, etc.

One glass of it you shall not get, etc.

We are all King George's men, etc.

What care we for King George's men! etc.

How many miles to Glasgow Lee? etc.

Sixty, seventy, eighty-three, etc.

Will I be there gin candle-licht? etc.

Just if your feet be clean and slicht, etc.

Open your gates and let me through, etc.

Not without a beck and a boo.

There's a beck and there's a boo,
Open your gates and let me through.

The players divide into two sides of equal number in lines facing
each other. Moving forward and backward the sides sing verse
about to the end upon which a struggle ensues to break through
each other's lines and reach a fixed goal on either side, the first to
arrive being the victors.   cf. 'King and Queen of Cantelon' (p. 123,
No. 402).

Other rhymes for this game, known variously as 'My Theerie
and My Thorie', 'Roman Soldiers' and 'French and English', contain other quantities as:

Have you any bread and wine? etc.

Yes, we have some bread and wine, etc.

Wc shall have one glass of it, etc.

Take one glass and go your way, etc.

We shall have two glasses of it, etc.
(and so on, up to five glasses)

We shall have a bottle of it, etc.

A bottle of it ye shall not have, etc.

We will break your glasses all, etc.

We will send for the magistrates, etc.

What care we for the magistrates! etc.

We will send for the policemen, etc.

What care we for the policemen! etc.

We will send for the red-coat men, etc.

What care we for the red-coat men! etc.

What kind of men are ye at all? etc.

We are all Prince Charlie's men, etc.

But what kind of men are ye at all? etc.

We are all King George's men, etc.

Are ye for a battle of it? etc.

Yes, we're for a battle of it,
A battle of it, a battle of it,
Yes, we're for a battle of it,
    My theerie and my thorie.

Another version is

Will you have a gill of ale?
    We are the Romans!
Will you have a gill of ale?
    For we are the Roman soldiers!

A gill of ale won't serve us all,
    We are the English!
A gill of ale won't serve us all,
    For we are the English soldiers!

Take a pint and go your way, etc.

A pint of ale won't serve us all, etc.

(*Similarly for a quart and a gallon, then*)

Take a barrel and go your way, etc.

A barrel of ale will serve us all,
    We are the English!
A barrel of ale will serve us all,
    For we are the English soldiers!

68

The rule for judging and buying horses with white feet

If he has one, buy him;
If he has two, try him;
If he has three, look about him;
If he has four, come without him.

69

I'll sing you one-oh!
    Green grow the rashes oh!
What is your one-oh?
    One is one and all alone,
    And ever more shall be so.

I'll sing you two-oh!
    Green grow the rashes oh!
What is your two-oh?
    Two, two, the lily-white boys,
    Clothed all in green-oh!
    One is one and all alone,
    And ever more shall be so.

(And so on, up to the last verse which begins slowly but at 'Nine'
speeds up until each singer is racing against the others to get to the end first.)

Twelve for the twelve Apostles,
Eleven for the eleven who went to Heaven,
And ten for the Ten Commandments,
Nine for the nine bright shiners,
Eight for the April rainers,
Seven for the seven stars in the sky,
And six for the echoing waters;
Five for the symbols at your door,
And four for the Gospel-makers.
Three, three are rivals,
Two, two, the lily-white boys,
Clothed all in green-oh!
One is one and all alone,
And evermore shall be so.

70

I've a kistie,
I've a creel,
I've a baggie
Fu' o' meal.

I've a doggie
At the door,
One, two,
Three, four.

71

I warn ye ance, I warn ye twice;
I warn ye three times over;
I warn ye a' t' be witty and wise
An' flee frae Johnny Rover.

One player is chosen to be Johnny Rover. When the rhyme is finished the other players run off, pursued by Johnny Rover. The first to be caught becomes Rover in turn.

72

My father left me just all he was able,
One bowl, one bottle, one label,
Two bowls, two bottles, two labels,
Three bowls, etc.

(*And so on* ad lib. *until the first breath gives out.*)

73

A finger count

Old Joe Badger had a little Indian,
Old Joe Badger had a little Indian,
Old Joe Badger had a little Indian,
    One little Indian boy.
He had one, he had two, he had three little Indians,
Four little, five little, six little Indians,
Seven little, eight little, nine little Indians,
    Ten little Indian boys.

Old Joe Badger had a little Indian,
Old Joe Badger had a little Indian,
Old Joe Badger had a little Indian,
    One little Indian boy.
He had ten, he had nine, he had eight little Indians,
Seven little, six little, five little Indians,
Four little, three little, two little Indians,
    One little Indian boy.

74

Counting sneezes

> One, a wish,
> Two, a kiss,
> Three, a letter,
> Four for something better.

cf.

> One, a wish,
> Two, a kiss,
> Three, a disappointment.

75

A race-start

> One for the money,
> Two for the show,
> Three to make ready,
> And four to go.

76

A button-count

> One, I love,
> Two, I love,
> Three, I love, I say.
> Four, I love with all my heart;
> Five, I cast away.
> Six, he loves,
> Seven, she loves;
> Eight, both love;
> Nine, he comes;
> Ten, he tarries;
> Eleven, he courts, and
> Twelve, he marries.

77

One man went to mow,
Went to mow a meadow,
One man and his dog,
Went to mow a meadow.

Two men went to mow,
Went to mow a meadow,
Two men, one man and his dog,
Went to mow a meadow.
            ad lib.

78

One, one, the day is done.
Two, two, so falls the dew.
Three, three, the moon I see.
Four, four, I'll play no more.

79

A counting-out rhyme

One potato, two potatoes,
Three potatoes, four;
Five potatoes, six potatoes,
Seven potatoes, more.
O.U.T. spells out.

80

A race start

One to be ready
Two to be steady
Three to be off!

cf. A version for learning to walk

One to make ready,
And two to prepare;
Good luck to the rider,
And away goes the mare!

81

A very short counting-out rhyme

One, two,
Sky blue.
All out
But you.

82

One, two, buckle my shoe;
Three, four, shut the door;
Five, six, pick up sticks;
Seven, eight, lay them straight;
Nine, ten, a good fat hen;
Eleven, twelve, dig and delve,
Thirteen, fourteen, maids a-courting;
Fifteen, sixteen, maids in the kitchen;
Seventeen, eighteen, maids in waiting;
Nineteen, twenty, my plate's empty.

83

One, two, kittens that mew;
Two, three, birds on a tree;
Three, four, shells from the shore;
Four, five, bees from the hive;
Five, six, little hayricks;
Six, seven, rooks in the heaven;
Seven, eight, sheep at the gate.

84

One, two, three,
Tommy hurt his knee.
He couldn't slide
And so he cried.
Out goes he.

85

One, two, three, a bumble bee
Stung a man upon the knee,
Stung a pig upon the snout,
Oh no, Johnny, you are out.

86

A ball-bouncing rhyme

One, two, three a-leerie,
Four, five, six a-leerie,
Seven, eight, nine a-leerie,
Ten a-leerie, postman.

The ball is bounced three times, the fourth time it is bounced under the leg, right and left leg being raised alternately at 'a-leerie'. After 'ten a-leerie' the ball is thrown up against a wall and the thrower turns completely round before catching it on the word 'postman'.

87

One, two, three,
My mother caught a flea,
She peppered it and salted it
And gave it to me for my tea.

cf.

One, two, three,
Nanny caught a flea;
The flea died; and Nanny cried,
'Out goes she'.

88

One, two, three, four,
Mary at the cottage door.
Five, six, seven, eight,
Eating cherries off a plate.

(A variant of the last line is

Mary at the garden gate.)

cf.

One, two, three, four,
Mary at the cottage door,
Eating cherries off a plate,
Down fell the summer seat.

89

One, two, three, four, five,
I caught a fish alive:
Six, seven, eight, nine, ten,
I let him go again.
Why did you let him go?
Because he bit my finger so!
Which finger did he bite?
The little finger on the right!

90

One, two, three, four, five, six, seven,
All good children go to heaven;
When they die their sin's forgiven,
One, two, three, four, five, six, seven.

or

One, two, three, four, five, six, seven,
All good children go to heaven:
A penny by the water,
Tuppence by the sea,
Threepence on the railway,
    Out goes she!

or

One, two, three, four, five, six, seven,
All good folks will go to heaven.
Peter and Paul,
Great and small,
You and me,
One, two, three,
Out goes he.

91

Porridge for one,
Porridge for two,
I shall be done
Long before you.

92

To spell 'potatoes' without any letters

Put 1 O; put 2 O's; put 3 O's;
Put 4 O's; put 5 O's; put 6 O's;
Put 7 O's; put 8 O's;—Potatoes.

93

Seven black friars, sitting back to back,
Fished from the bridge for a pike or a jack.
The first caught a tiddler,
The second caught a crab,
The third caught a winkle,
The fourth caught a dab,
The fifth caught a tadpole,
The sixth caught an eel,
The seventh one caught an old cart-wheel.

94

To be said very quickly

Seventeen, sixteen, fifteen,
Fourteen, thirteen, twelve,
Eleven, ten, nine,
Eight, seven, six,
Five, four, three,
The tenor o' the tune plays merrilie.

95

The animals came in two by two,
    Vive la compagnie.
The centipede with the kangaroo,
    Vive la compagnie.
One more river, and that's the river of Jordan,
One more river, there's one more river to cross.

The animals came in three by three,
    Vive la compagnie.
The elephant on the back of the flea,
    Vive la compagnie.
One more river, etc.

The animals came in four by four,
    Vive la compagnie.
The camel he got stuck in the door,
    Vive la compagnie.
One more river, etc.

The animals came in five by five,
Some were dead, and some were alive.

The animals came in six by six,
The monkey he was up to his tricks.

The animals came in seven by seven,
Some went to Hell, and some went to Heaven.

The animals came in eight by eight,
The worm was early, the bird was late.

The animals came in nine by nine,
Some had water and some had wine.

The animals came in ten by ten,
    Vive la compagnie.
If you want any more you must sing it again,
    Vive la compagnie.
One more river, and that's the river of Jordan,
One more river, there's one more river to cross.

96

The first day of Christmas,
My true love sent to me
A partridge in a pear-tree.

The second day of Christmas
My true love sent to me
Two turtle doves and
A partridge in a pear-tree.

    (*and so on, up to*)

The twelfth day of Christmas,
My true love sent to me
Twelve lords a-leaping,
Eleven ladies dancing,
Ten pipers piping,
Nine drummers drumming,
Eight maids a-milking,
Seven swans a-swimming,
Six geese a-laying,
Five gold rings,
Four colly birds,
Three French hens,
Two turtle doves, and
A partridge in a pear-tree.

97

The king sent his lady on the first Yule day,
A papingo-aye;
Wha learns my carol and carries it away?

The king sent his lady on the second Yule day,
Three partridges, a papingo-aye;
Wha learns my carol and carries it away?

(*and so on, up to*)

The king sent his lady on the thirteenth Yule day,
Three stalks o' merry corn,
Three maids a-merry dancing,
Three hinds a-merry hunting,
An Arabian baboon,
Three swans a-merry swimming,
Three ducks a-merry laying,
A bull that was brown,
Three gold spinks,
Three starlings,
A goose that was grey,
Three plovers,
Three partridges,
A papingo-aye;
Wha learns my carol and carries it away?

98

This old man, he played one,
He played nick-nack on my drum,
With a nick-nack paddy-wack
Give a dog a bone,
This old man went rolling home.

Two— on my shoe.

Three— on my knee.

Four— on my door.

Five— on my hive.

Six— on my sticks.

Seven— up to heaven.

99

Three craws sat upon a wa', sat upon a wa',
Three craws sat upon a wa',
  On a cold and frosty morning.

The first craw flee-eed awa', flee-eed awa',
The first craw flee-eed awa',
  On a cold and frosty morning.

The second craw fleed awa' an' a', fleed awa' an' a',
The second craw fleed awa' an' a',
  On a cold and frosty morning.

The third craw wasna there at a', wasna there at a',
The third craw wasna there at a',
  On a cold and frosty morning.

cf.

The first craw fell and broke his jaw,
  Fell and broke his jaw, etc.

The second craw couldna see at a', etc.

The third craw wasna there at a', etc.

100

Twa afore ane,
'Three afore five,
Noo ane an' than ane,
And fower comes belive.
First twa and than twa,
And three at a cast,
Double ane and twice twa,
And Jockie at the last.

101

Twelve huntsmen with horns and hounds,
· Hunting over other men's grounds;
Eleven ships sailing o'er the main,
Some bound for France and some for Spain:
I wish them all safe home again:
Ten comets in the sky,
Some low and some high:

D

Nine peacocks in the air,
I wonder how they all came there.
I do not know and I do not care;
Eight joiners in Joiners' Hall,
Working with the tools and all;
Seven lobsters in a dish,
As fresh as any heart could wish;
Six beetles against the wall,
Close by an old woman's apple-stall;
Five puppies of our dog Ball,
Who daily for their breakfast call;
Four horses stuck in a bog,
Three monkeys tied to a clog;
Two pudding-ends would choke a dog,
With a gaping, wide-mouthed, waddling frog.

102

When I was ane, I was in my skin;
When I was twa, I ran awa';
When I was three, I could climb a tree;
When I was four, they dang me o'er;
When I was five, I didna thrive;
When I was sax, I got my cracks;
When I was seven, I could count eleven;
When I was aught, I was laid straught;
When I was nine, I could write a line;
When I was ten, I could mend a pen;
When I was eleven, I gaed to the weaving;
When I was twall, I was brosy Wull.

MEASURE

103

Churn the buttermilk, quick, quick, quick,
I owe my mother a pint of milk.

A rhyme for a game to be played on the sand as the tide goes out leaving it soft. The player turns half way round as he says the words, his heel sinking into the hollow he makes.

104

Boys riding upon each other's backs

Cripple Dick upon a stick,
Sandy on a soo,
Ride away to Galloway,
To buy a pund o' woo'.

105

Frae Wibleton tae Wableton
It's sixteen miles;
And frae Wableton tae Wibleton
It's sixteen miles;
Back again an fore again
It's thirty-twa miles,
This wey an that wey,
And baith weys whiles.

106

Half a pound of tuppenny rice,
Half a pound of treacle;
That's the way the money goes,
Pop goes the weasel!

107

How many beans make five?
One and another;
Two and t'other!

108

I had a little pony,
They ca'd it Dapple Gray;
I lent it to a lady,
To ride a mile away.

She whipped it, she lashed it,
She ca'd it owre the brae;
I winna lend my pony mair,
Though a' the ladies pray.

109

I had a little sister,
Her name was Pretty Peep;
She wades in the waters
Deep, deep, deep!
She climbs up the mountains
High, high, high!
My poor little sister,
She has but one eye.

Answer: A star.

110

I ring, I ring, a pinky!
If I tell a lee
I'll go tae the bad place
Whenever I dee.
White pan, black pan,
Burn me tae death,
Tak a muckle gully
An' cut ma breath,
Ten miles below the earth.   Amen!

111

Madam, I will give you a fine silken gown,
Nine yards wide and eleven yards long,
If you will be my gay ladye.

Sir, I won't accept your fine silken gown,
Nine yards wide and eleven yards long,
Nor will I be your gay ladye.

John, my man, how can this matter be?
I love a lady who doesn't love me,
　　Nor will she be my gay ladye.

Peace, master, peace; you need not fear
She'll be your love and only dear,
　　But the gold ring only will gain you her.

Madam, I'll give you a fine golden ring,
To go to church to be married in,
　　If you will be my gay ladye.

Sir, I will accept your fine golden ring,
To go to church to be married in,
　　And I will be your gay ladye.

John, my man, here's a crown for thee,
For winning me this gay ladye.

cf. p. 48, No. 132.

112

　　Moon, moon,
　　Mak me a pair o' shoon,
　　And I'll dance till you be done.

113

　　Old Farmer Giles,
　　He went seven miles,
　　With his faithful dog, Old Rover;
　　And Old Farmer Giles,
　　When he came to the stiles,
　　Took a run and jumped clean over.

114

　　Round and round ran a wee hare.
　　One span—two spans—
　　Tickle you under there.

A tickling game which starts with a circular movement in the palm of the hand. The spans are measured up the arm of the child being tickled and the last line brings the tickler's finger to the armpit, or under the ear.

115

There was a crooked man, and he went a crooked mile,
He found a crooked sixpence against a crooked stile:
He bought a crooked cat, which caught a crooked mouse,
And they all lived together in a little crooked house.

116

Twelve inches make a foot.
Of our table that's the root.
Three feet in every yard;
Let us measure, it's not hard.

117

What's a score?
Ten and ten more.

MONEY

118

About the bush, Willy,
    About the beehive,
About the bush, Willy,
    I'll meet thee alive.

Then to my ten shillings
    Add you but a groat,
I'll go to Newcastle,
    And buy a new coat.

Five and five shillings
    Five and a crown;
Five and five shillings
    Will buy a new gown.

Five and five shillings,
    Five and a groat;
Five and five shillings
    Will buy a new coat.

119

A ha'penny here, and a ha'penny there,
Fourpence ha'penny and a ha'penny mair;
A ha'penny wat, and a ha'penny dry,
Fourpence ha'penny and a ha'penny forby—
    How much is that?

Answer: A shilling.

120

A counting-out rhyme

    A ha'penny puddin', a ha'penny pie;
    Stand ye—there—out—by.

121

A pin to see the poppy show,
A pin to see a die,
A pin to see an old man,
Sitting in the sky.

Flowers are pressed or coloured pictures pasted beneath a sheet
of glass, which is laid upon a piece of paper in which a flap is cut.
The charge for seeing the show is a pin.

Pins are—or were—the proper currency of youth, and therefore
rightly take their place here in this section with less innocent lucre.

Other forms of currency are contained in 'Wha'll try the lucky
kyle? A preen, a bool or a button a shot?' in which a player is
invited to knock down a 'kyle' (a long narrow bobbin) by trundling
a marble from a short distance.

cf. 'Dab a prin in my lottery book' (p. 47, No. 125), and 'I'll gie
you a pennyworth o' preens' (p. 48, No. 132).

122

As I went up the garden,
I found a little farthing;
I gave it to my mother,
To buy a little brother.
My brother was a sailor,
He sailed across the sea,
And all the fish that he could catch
Were one, two, three.

123

Buttons a farthing a pair,
Come, who will buy them of me?
They are round and sound and pretty,
And fit for girls of the city.
Come, who will buy them of me?
Buttons a farthing a pair.

124

*A game played 'running under a handkerchief', something like 'Oranges and
Lemons'*

Currants and raisins a penny a pound,
Three days holiday.

125

Dab a prin in my lottery book;
Dab ane, dab twa,
Dab a' your prins awa'.

A pin is stuck into a book, between some pages of which small pictures or scraps have been placed. If the pin enters between two pages containing a picture the pricker gains the picture and pays the pin for it.

126

Gay go up and gay go down,
To ring the bells of London town.
Halfpence and farthings,
Say the bells of St. Martin's.
Oranges and lemons,
Say the bells of St. Clement's.
Pancakes and fritters,
Say the bells of St. Peter's.
Two sticks and an apple,
Say the bells of Whitechapel.
Kettles and pans,
Say the bells of St. Ann's.
You owe me ten shillings,
Say the bells of St. Helen's.
When will you pay me?
Say the bells of Old Bailey.
When I grow rich,
Say the bells of Shoreditch.
Pray when will that be?
Say the bells of Stepney.
I am sure I don't know,
Says the great bell of Bow.

127

Green cheeses, yellow laces,
Up and down the market places;
First a penny and then a groat,
Turn, cheeses, turn.

Girls spin round and round till their dresses fly out at the bottom and then suddenly squat down so that the air under the dress causes the skirt to bulge out like a balloon.

128

Here's a string o' wild geese,
　How mony for a penny?
Ane to my lord,
　And ane to my lady;
Up the gate and down the gate,
　They're a' flown frae me!

129

Here's Finiky Hawkes,
As busy as any,
Will well black your shoes,
And charge but a penny.

130

Hey Johnny Raw, dae ye no think it shame,
Coortin' a lass that's no yer ain,
Wi' a bawbee watch an' a ha'penny chain?
I wish yer Granny saw ye!

131

Honey-pots, honey-pots, all in a row,
Twenty-five shillings wherever you go.
Who'll buy my honey-pots?

This is one of several rhymes for the game of 'Honey pots', in which one child clasps his hands under his knees while two others lift him by the armpits and swing him to and fro. If his hands remain clasped throughout the verse he is a good honey-pot.

132

'I'll gie you a pennyworth o' preens,
That's aye the way that love begins;
If ye'll walk with me, leddy, leddy,
If ye'll walk with me, leddy.'

'I'll no hae your pennyworth o' preens,
That's no the way that love begins;
And I'll no walk with you, with you,
And I'll no walk with you.'

'O Johnnie, O Johnnie, what can the matter be,
That I love this leddy, and she loves na me?
And for her sake I must die, must die,
And for her sake I must die.'

'I'll gie you a bonny silver box,
With seven silver hinges, and seven silver locks,
If ye'll walk, etc.'

'I'll no hae your bonnie silver box,
With seven silver hinges, and seven silver locks,
And I'll no walk, etc.'
    (*Repeat third verse*)

'But I'll gie you a bonnier silver box,
With seven golden hinges, and seven golden locks,
If ye'll walk, etc.'

'I'll no hae your bonnier silver box, etc.
    (*Repeat third verse*)

'I'll gie you a pair o' bonny shoon,
The tane made in Sodom, the tother in Rome,
If ye'll walk, etc.'

'I'll no hae your pair o' bonny shoon, etc.
    (*Repeat third verse*)

'I'll gie you the half o' Bristol town,
With coaches rolling up and down,
If ye'll walk, etc.'

'I'll no hae the half o' Bristol town, etc.
    (*Repeat third verse*)

'I'll gie you the hale o' Bristol town,
With coaches rolling up and down,
If ye'll walk with me, leddy, leddy,
If ye'll walk with me, leddy.'

'If ye'll gie me the hale o' Bristol town,
With coaches rolling up and down,
I will walk with you, with you,
    And I will walk with you.'

This is the story of the proud lady who met Auld Nick himself,
and the climax is that 'aff he flew wi' her'.

133

I'll sing you a song,
Though not very long,
Yet I think it as pretty as any;
Put your hand in your purse
You'll never be worse
And give the poor singer a penny.

134

Turn about the basket

Jenny Mac, Jenny Mac, Jenny Macghie,
Turn your back about to me,
And if you find an ill bawbee,
Lift it up and gie't to me.

Two girls cross their arms behind their backs, and thus taking
hold of each other's hands, parade along together, occasionally
turning upon their arms, as indicated in the rhyme.

135

Another rhyme for this amusement is

A basket, a basket, a bonny penny basket,
A penny to you, and a penny to me,
Turn about the basket.

See also p. 127, No. 412.

136

Laddie wi' the shelly-coat,
Help me owre the ferry-boat;
The ferry-boat's owre dear,
Ten pounds every year.

137

Long leather laces
A penny a pair.
If you want to buy them
Go to Johnny Blair.
There you'll see an old man
Sitting on a chair,
Selling long leather laces
A penny a pair.

138

Lucy Locket lost her pocket,
Kitty Fisher found it,
But ne'er a penny was there in it
Except the binding round it.

139

Needle cases, needle cases, in a silver saucer.
Who shall I direct it to but Captain ——'s daughter?
What will you give to tell her name, tell her name,
    tell her name?
A hundred pounds and a glass of wine.

    (*The girl's name is given and she then asks*)

What will you give to tell his name?

    (*The others reply*)

Two hundred pounds and a glass of wine.

    (*Boy's name given by girl*)

As I gaed down to borrow a pan,
I saw her sitting kissing her man;
She off with the glove and on with the ring.
To-morrow, to-morrow the wedding begins.
Clean the brass candlesticks, clean the fireside,
Draw up the curtains and let's see the bride.

The players stand in a circle with one, holding a handkerchief,
in the middle. She sings the first lines. When the girl named has
told her her sweetheart's name she sits down in the centre and
covers her face with her hands while the handkerchief holder goes
round again asking the next question, to which the circle replies.
After the boy's name has been given the handkerchief holder goes
round singing the last lines.

140

Ride a cock horse to Banbury Cross
To see what Johnny can buy.
A penny white cake
I'll buy for his sake,
And a twopenny tart or a pie.

141

Seesaw, Margery Daw,
Johnny shall have a new master,
And he shall have but a penny a day,
Because he can't work any faster.

cf.

> See-saw
> Jack-a-daw
> Whit is a craw
> Tae dae wi' her?

> She hasna a stockin'
> Tae pit on her,
> And the craw hasna ane
> For tae gie her.

142

Simple Simon met a pieman
  Going to the fair;
Said Simple Simon to the pieman,
  'Let me taste your ware.'

Said the pieman to Simple Simon,
  'Show me first your penny.'
Said Simple Simon to the pieman,
  'Indeed I have not any.'

Simple Simon went a-fishing
  For to catch a whale;
All the water he had got
  Was in his mother's pail.

Simple Simon went to look
  If plums grew on a thistle;
He pricked his fingers very much,
  Which made poor Simon whistle.

143

Sing a song of sixpence,
  A pocket full of rye;
Four-and-twenty blackbirds,
  Baked in a pie.
When the pie was opened,
  The birds began to sing,
Was not that a dainty dish
  To set before a King?

The King was in his counting-house,
  Counting out his money;
The Queen was in the parlour
  Eating bread and honey;
The maid was in the garden,
  Hanging out the clothes,
When down came a blackbird,
  And pecked off her nose.

144

Sing song! Merry go round,
  Here we go up to the moon, oh!
Little Johnny a penny has found,
  And so we'll sing a tune, oh!

What shall I buy,
  Johnnie did cry,
With the penny I've found,
  So bright and round?

What shall you buy?
A kite that will fly
Up to the moon, all through the sky!
But when it gets there,
If it stay in the air,
Or the man up in the moon, oh!
Should open the door,
And take it in with his paw—
We'd sing to another tune, oh!

145

A waterman's rhyme, traditional

Twopence to London Bridge, threepence to the Strand,
Fourpence, Sir, to Whitehall Stairs, or else you'll go by land.

146

Up and down the market,
Selling penny buns,
One a penny, two a penny,
Three a penny buns.

TIME

(1) Hours of the Day

147

The cock doth crow
To let you know
If you be wise
'Tis time to rise.

148

A dillar, a dollar,
A ten o'clock scholar,
What makes you come so soon?
You used to come at nine o'clock,
But now you come at noon.

149

Bell horses, bell horses,
What time of day?
One o'clock, two o'clock,
Three and away.

Bell horses, bell horses,
What time of day?
Two o'clock, three o'clock,
Four and away.

Bell horses, bell horses,
What time of day?
Five o'clock, six o'clock,
Now time to stay.

A running game in which two or three children join hands, as for 'Auld Lang Syne', and run in time to the chant until the last word. A. B. Gomme says, 'The children form long trains, standing one behind the other. They march and sing till the last line is reached, when they stand, and begin again as before'.

150

Between the hours of ten and two
Will show you what the day will do.

151

Cam' ye by the salmon fishers?
Cam' ye by the roperee?
Saw ye a sailor laddie
Waiting on the coast for me?
I ken far I'm gyain,
I ken fa's gyain wi' me,
I ha'e a lad o' my ain,
Ye daurna tak' him fae me.
Stockings of blue silk,
Shoes of patent leather,
Kid to tie them up,
And gold rings on his finger.
Oh for six o'clock!
Oh for seven I'm weary!
Oh for eight o'clock!
And then I'll see my dearie.

The children join hands and dance round in a circle to the song.

152

Chickidy hand,
Chickidy hand,
The Warner, my Cock,
Crows at four in the morning.

or

Stag, stag arony,
Ma dog's bony,
Them 'at I catch
'll ha' to go wi' me.

or

Warning once, warning twice,
Warning three times over;
When the cock crows out come!
Whiddy, whiddy, wake-cock. Warning.

or

Over clover,
Nine times over.

These are rhymes for a form of 'Tig' in which the player who is 'Tig' must touch his first victim while keeping his hands clasped with the two forefingers extended. He then joins hands with his captive, and they pursue the others; those whom they catch also join hands till they form a long line.

153

The rhyme for 'Hunt the Slipper'

Cobbler, cobbler, mend my shoe,
Get it done by half-past two;
Half-past two is much too late,
Get it done by half-past eight.

Another version runs

'Cobbler, cobbler, mend my shoe.
Have it done by half past two.
Stitch it up and stitch it down.'
'That will cost you half a crown.'

154

Dormy, dormy, dormouse
Sleeps in his little house.
He won't wake up
Till supper-time
And that won't be
Till half-past nine.

155

Do you ken Elsie Marley, honey?
The wife who sells the barley, honey?
She won't get up to serve her swine,
And do you ken Elsie Marley, honey?

Elsie Marley is grown so fine
She won't get up to serve the swine,
But lies in bed till eight or nine,
And surely she does take her time.

Do you ken Elsie Marley, honey?
The wife who sells the barley, honey?
She won't get up to serve her swine,
And do you ken Elsie Marley, honey?

156

Early to bed and early to rise
Makes a man healthy, wealthy and wise.

157

A skipping rhyme

Every morning at eight o'clock,
You all may hear the postman's knock.
One, two, three, four, there goes . . .

A better version of this is as follows

Every morning at eight o'clock
You can hear the postman's knock.
Up jumps Mary to open the door.
One letter, two letters, three letters, four.

The child named runs out of the rope at the last word and another enters.

Another skipping game involving a count is 'Winding the Clock' in which the skipper counts up to twelve, turning round each time she jumps or skips. Both of these require two players to turn the rope for the skipper.

See also: 'Feetikin, feetikin, when will ye gang?' (p. 5, No. 2).

158

He that would thrive
Must rise at five;
He that hath thriven
May lie till seven;
And he that by the plough would thrive,
Himself must either hold or drive.

159

A tickling rhyme

Hickory, dickory, dock,
The mouse ran up the clock.
The clock struck One,
The mouse ran down,
Hickory, dickory, dock.

160

How dan, dilly dow,
    How den dan,
Weel were your minny
    An ye were a man.

Ye would hunt and hawk,
    And haud her o' game,
And water your daddy's horse
    I' the mill dam.

How dan, dilly dow,
    How dan flours,
Ye'se lie i' your bed
    Till eleven hours.

If at eleven hours
    You list to rise,
Ye'se hae your dinner dight
    In a new guise;

Lav'rocks' legs
    And titlins' taes,
And a' sic dainties
    My mannie shall hae.

161

I'll away to t' beck to wash my neck.
When I get there I'll ask t' ould dame
what o'clock it is?
It's one, and you'll be hanged at two.

(*Repeated up to*)

It's eleven and you'll be hanged at twelve.

The players march round one of their number in single file,
holding on to each other and saying the first two lines, to which
the one in the middle replies with the third. At the last verse they
run in all directions and the Old Dame tries to catch one who in
turn becomes Old Dame.

162

Lingle, lingle, lang tang,
Our cat's dead!
What did she die wi'?
Wi' a sair head!

A' you that kent her
When she was alive,
Come to her burial
Atween four and five!

A childish parody of the usual form in which a death was an-
nounced by the town-crier.

cf.

Ding dang, bell rang
Cattie's in the well, man.
Fa' dang her in, man?
Jean and Sandie Din, man.
Fa' took her out, man?
Me and Willie Cout, man,
A' them that kent her
When she was alive,
Come to the burialie
Between four and five.

163

The hours of sleep

Nature needs but five,
Custom gives thee seven;
Laziness takes nine,
And Wickedness eleven.

164

Past three o'clock
And a fine frosty morning.

In his *Diary* for January 16, 1660, Mr Pepys records, 'I staid up
till the bellman came by with his bell just under my window as I
was writing of this very line, and cried,

'Past one of the clock,
And a cold, frosty, windy morning.'

165

Sneel, Snaul,
Robbers are coming to pull down your wall;
Sneel, Snaul,
Put out your horn,
Robbers are coming to steal your corn,
Coming at four o'clock in the morn.

166

The moon shines bright,
And the stars gie a light,
We'll see to kiss a bonny lass
At ten o'clock at night.

167

Wee Willie Winkie runs through the town,
Upstairs and downstairs in his nightgown,
Rapping at the window, crying through the lock,
'Are the children in their beds, for now it's eight o'clock?'

168

We've come to see poor Jenny Jones, poor Jenny Jones, poor
    Jenny Jones,
We've come to see poor Jenny Jones. How is she to-day?

Poor Jenny is washing, washing, washing,
Poor Jenny is washing, washing hard to-day.

What time can we see her? At one o'clock.

We've come to see poor Jenny Jones, etc.

Poor Jenny is starching, etc.

When can we see her? At two o'clock.

We've come to see poor Jenny Jones, etc.

Poor Jenny is folding, etc.

When can we see her? At three o'clock.

We've come to see poor Jenny Jones, etc.

Poor Jenny is ironing, etc.

When can we see her? At four o'clock.

We've come to see poor Jenny Jones, etc.

Poor Jenny is poorly, etc.

When can we see her? At five o'clock.

We've come to see poor Jenny Jones, etc.

Poor Jenny is dying, etc.

When shall we see her? Come at six o'clock.

We've come to see poor Jenny Jones, etc.

Poor Jenny is dead, dead, dead,
Poor Jenny is dead, you can't see her to-day.

What colour will you have for the funeral for poor Jenny
    Jones?

Red?

Red is for the soldiers, soldiers, soldiers,
Red is for the soldiers, and that won't do.

Blue?

Blue is for the sailors, etc.

Pink?

Pink is for the babies, etc.

White?

White is for a wedding, etc.

Black?

Black is for the mourners, mourners, mourners,
Black is for the mourners, and that will do.

Poor Jenny Jones is dead, dead, dead,
Poor Jenny Jones is dead, and lies in her grave.

This is one variant for an action game in which the dialogue is conducted by the players divided into two sides, one of which contains the girl chosen to represent Jenny Jones, or by two girls representing Jenny, who performs the actions ascribed to her, and the Mother who replies to the questions of the remaining players.

TIME

(ii) The Days of the Week

169

A rhyme for cutting finger-nails

Cut them on Monday, you cut them for health;
Cut them on Tuesday, you cut them for wealth;
Cut them on Wednesday, you cut them for news;
Cut them on Thursday, a new pair of shoes;
Cut them on Friday, you cut them for sorrow;
Cut them on Saturday, see your true-love to-morrow;
Cut them on Sunday, ill-luck will be with you all the week.

170

Monday alone,
Tuesday together,
Wednesday we walk
When it's fine weather,
Thursday we kiss,
Friday we cry,
Saturday's hours
Seem almost to fly.
But of all the days in the week
We will call
Sunday, the rest day,
The best day of all.

171

Monday's child is fair of face,
Tuesday's child is full of grace,
Wednesday's child is full of woe,
Thursday's child has far to go,
Friday's child is loving and giving,
Saturday's child works hard for its living;
But the child that is born on the Sabbath day
Is wise and wonderful, blithe and gay.

172

Sneeze on Monday, sneeze for danger;
Sneeze on Tuesday, kiss a stranger;
Sneeze on Wednesday, get a letter;
Sneeze on Thursday, something better;
Sneeze on Friday, sneeze for sorrow;
Sneeze on Saturday, see your sweetheart to-morrow.

173

Solomon Grundy,
Born on Monday,
Christened on Tuesday,
Married on Wednesday,
Ill on Thursday,
Worse on Friday,
Died on Saturday,
Buried on Sunday.
That was the end of Solomon Grundy.

174

They that wash on Monday
Hae a' the week tae dry.
They that wash on Tuesday
Are no faur by.
They that wash on Wednesday
Are no sair tae mean.
They that wash on Thursday
May get their claes clean.
They that wash on Friday
Hae gey muckle need.
They that wash on Saturday
Are dirty daws indeed.

cf. the English version

They that wash on Monday
Have all the week to dry;
They that wash on Tuesday
Are not so much awry;
They that wash on Wednesday
Are not so much to blame;

They that wash on Thursday
 Wash for shame;
They that wash on Friday
 Wash in need;
And they that wash on Saturday,
 Oh! they're sluts indeed.

175

How many days has my baby to play?
Saturday, Sunday, Monday,
Tuesday, Wednesday, Thursday, Friday,
Saturday, Sunday, Monday.

176

Monday flit,
Never sit.

cf.

A Friday's flit
Will not long sit.

and

Saturday's flit
Will never sit.

177

On Thursday at three
Look out and you'll see
What Friday will be.

cf.

Friday's noon
Is Sunday's doom.

178

A Friday's sail
Always fail.

179

Friday night's dream
On the Saturday told,
Is sure to come true,
Be it never so old.

180

Friday's a day as'll have his trick,
The fairest or foulest day o' the week.

181

Friday's hair and Sunday's horn
Go to the Devil on Monday morn.

It is unlucky to cut hair or nails on Friday or Sunday.

cf.

Sunday shaven,
Sunday shorn,
Better hadst thou ne'er been born.

182

Such as a Friday,
Such is a Sunday.

183

A Saturday's moon,
If it comes once in seven years, it comes too soon.

cf.

On Saturday new, on Sunday full,
Was never good and never wooll.

and

A Saturday's change* brings the boat to the door;
But a Sunday's change brings it upon t' mid-floor.
(*of moon)

and

A Saturday's moon and a Sunday's prime
Never brought good in any man's time.

184

On Saturday night
Shall be all my care
To powder my locks
And curl my hair.

On Sunday morning
My love will come in,
When he will marry me
With a gold ring.

185

This is siller Saturday,
The morn's the resting-day;
Monanday up and till't again,
And Tyesday push away.

186

Sally go round the stars,
Sally go round the moon.
Sally go round the stars
On a Sunday afternoon.

(or: On Saturday afternoon.)

The players join hands and dance round to the song, reversing direction when they have sung it through.

TIME

(III) THE YEAR

COUNTRY rhymes about the weather and the work of the various months of the year vary with the district; the first line of one is united with the second of another, and so on in an almost endless process of combination and permutation. The following list is by no means complete.

187

A Januar haddock,
A Februar bannock,
And a March pint o' ale.

The best season for these things, but compare

A cameral haddock's ne'er guid
Till it get three draps o' May flude.

188

A January opring
Is worth naething.

189

If Janiveer's calends be summerly gay
'Twill be winterly weather till the calends of May.

190

If one knew how good it were
To eat a hen in Janivere,
Had he twenty in the flock,
He'd leave but one to go with the cock.

191

If the grass grow in Janiveer,
'Twill be the worse for't all the year.

192

In January if the sun appear,
March and April pay full dear.

193

The blackest month in all the year
Is the month of Janiveer.

194

All the months in the year
Curse a fair Februeer.

195

February, fill the dike,
Be it black, or be it white!
If it be white, it's the better to like!

196

February, if ye be fair,
The sheep will mend and nothing mair;
February, if ye be foul,
The sheep will die in every pool.

197

If February give much snow
A fine summer it doth foreshow.

198

A dry March, wet April and cool May
Fill barn, cellar, and bring much hay.

199

In beginning or in end,
March its gifts will send.

200

March brings the lammie
And buds the thorn,
But blows through the flint
Of an ox's horn.

201

March borrowed three days from Aprile,
And oh, but they were vile!
The first o' them was wind and weet,
The second, it was snaw and sleet;
The third o' them was sic a freeze,
It froze a' the birdies' nebs to the trees.

202

March said to Averil:
'I see three hoggs on yonder hill;
And if you'll lend me dayis three,
I'll find a way to gar them die!'
The first o' them was wind and weet;
The second o' them was snaw and sleet;
The third o' them was sic a freeze,
It froze the birds' feet to the trees.
When the three days were past and gane,
The silly poor hoggs came hirpling hame.

203

March will search, April will try,
May will tell ye if ye'll live or die.

204

March winds and April showers
Bring forth May flowers.

205

The first of March
The crows begin to search,
By the first of April
They are sitting still,
By the first of May
They're all flown away;
Coming greedy back again
With October's wind and rain.

cf.

In March the birds begin to search,
In April the corn begins to fill;
In May the birds begin to lay.

F

206

A cold April
The barn will fill.

207

A flood in April,
A flood in May,
And a flood to take away the hay.

cf.

An April flood,
Carries away the frog and her brood.

208

April comes in with his hack and his bill,
And sets a flower on every hill.

209

April weather,
Rain and sunshine both together.

210

Betwixt April and May if there be rain,
'Tis worth more than oxen and wain.

211

The Cuckoo

In April,
Come he will.
In May,
Sing all day.
In June,
Change his tune.
In July,
Prepare to fly.
In August,
Go he must!

212

In the month of Averil,
The gowk comes over the hill,
In a shower of rain.

The first cock of hay
Frights the cuckoo away!

213

The first day of April,
You may send a fool whither you will.

See also p. 85, No. 273.

214

Till April's dead
Change not a thread.

cf.

Ne'er cast a clout
Till May be out.

215

When April blows his horn*
It's good for hay and corn.
(* thunder)

216

A dry May and a dripping June
Bring all things into tune.

217

A snowstorm in May
Is worth a waggonload of hay.

218

A swarm of bees in May
Is worth a load of hay;
A swarm of bees in June
Is worth a silver spoon;
A swarm of bees in July
Is not worth a fly.

219

Come it early or come it late,
In May comes the cow-quake.*

(* trembling grass)

220

Cut a thistle in May,
It will grow next day;
Cut it in June,
It will grow again soon;
Cut in July,
It will surely die;
Cut in August,
Die it must.

cf.

Spud them in May,
They are up next day.
Spud them in June,
They come again soon.
Spud them in July,
Then they soon will die.

221

If you sweep the house with broom in May
You'll sweep the head of that house away.

222

Marry in May,
You'll rue it for aye.

223

Mist in May, and heat in June,
Maks the harvest richt sune.

224

Thun'er in May,
Hunger for aye.

225

To the twelfth of July from the twelfth of May
All is day.

226

Twenty-ninth of May
Royal-Oak Day.

227

Full early in the morning
Awakes the summer sun,
The month of June arriving,
The cold and night are done.
The cuckoo is a fine bird,
She whistles as she flies,
And as she whistles 'Cuckoo',
The bluer grow the skies.

228

June damp and warm
Does the farmer no harm.

229

Thun'er in June
Pits a' thing in tune.

230

A shower in July, when the corn begins to fill,
Is worth a plow of oxen, and all belongs theretill.

231

Bow-wow dandy fly,
Brew no beer in July.

232

If the first of July it be rainy weather,
'Twill rain, more or less, for four weeks together.

233

In July
Some reap rye;
In August
If one will not the other must.

234

Dry August and warm
Doth harvest no harm.

235

If the twenty-fourth of August be fair and clear,
Then hope for a prosperous autumn that year.

236

September, blow soft
Till the fruit's in the loft.

237

Good October, a good blast,
To blow the hog acorn and mast.

238

In October dung your field,
And your land its wealth shall yield.

239

If there's ice in November that will bear a duck,
There'll be nothing after but sludge and muck.

240

On the first of November, if the weather hold clear,
An end of wheat sowing do make for the year.

241

December's frost and January's flood
Never boded the husbandman's good.

242

Thirty days hath September,
  April, June and November,
All the rest have thirty-one
  Saving February alone.
Twenty-eight is all its store,
  And in Leap Year one day more.

243

Leap-year
Was never a good sheep year.

TIME

(IV) LENGTH OF TIME

244

As the days grow longer
The storms grow stronger.

245

As the days lengthen
The cold doth strengthen.

246

A sunshiny shower
Won't last half an hour.

247

Bourtree, bourtree, crooked rung,
Never straight, and never strong;
Ever bush and never tree,
Since our Lord was nailed to ye!

248

I had a little hen, the prettiest ever seen;
She washed me the dishes, and kept the house clean;
She went to the mill to fetch me some flour,
She brought it home in less than an hour;
She baked me my bread, she brewed me my ale;
She sat by the fire and told many a fine tale.

249

Pease porridge hot, pease porridge cold,
Pease porridge in a caup, nine days old.
Tell me that in four letters.

cf.

Pease porridge hot,
pease porridge cold,
Pease porridge in the pot,
nine days old.
Spell me *that* without a P,
and a scholar you will be.

250

Pease pudding hot,
Pease pudding cold,
Pease pudding in the pot,
Nine days old.

Some like it hot,
Some like it cold,
Some like it in the pot,
Nine days old.

251

Seven years a baby,
Seven years at school,
Seven years apprentice,
Seven years a fool.

252

Sunny, sunny shower,
Come on for half an hour;
Gar a' the hens cower,
Gar a' the sheep clap;
Gar ilka wife in Lammermuir
Look in her kail-pat.

253

There's pease and groats in my coat pouch,
They'll no come out this hour yet,
No this half,
No this half,
No this hale half hour yet.

254

Three wattles, a hound's life;
Three hounds, a steed;
Three steeds, a man;
Three men, an eagle;
Three eagles, a salmon;
Three salmon, a yew-tree;
Three yew-trees, a ridge;
Three ridges from the beginning to the
end of the world.

A wattle is a hedge-stake, supposed to last three years. A ridge is a plough division used in prehistoric times leaving an indelible mark on the countryside.

255

Tip top tower
Tumbled down in half-an-hour.

This may be a memory of the Tower of Babel. cf. 'Seven mile sank and seven mile fell' (p. 103, No. 332).

256

When I was a little boy
I had but little wit;
It is some time ago,
    And I've no more yet;
Nor ever, ever shall
    Until that I die,
For the longer I live
    The more fool am I.

FESTIVALS

257

Collop Monday,
Pancake Tuesday,
Ash Wednesday,
Bloody Thursday,
Lang Friday,
Hey for Seturday eftirnin;
Hey for Sunday
At twal o'clock
Whan a' the plum puddins
Jump oot o' the pot.

258

Christmas comes but once a year,
And when it comes it brings good cheer.

259

Christmas is a-coming, the geese are getting fat,
Please to put a penny in the old man's hat;
If you haven't got a penny, a ha'penny will do,
If you haven't got a ha'penny, God bless you.

260

Dame, get up and bake your pies,
Bake your pies, bake your pies;
Dame, get up and bake your pies,
On Christmas Day in the morning.

Dame, what makes your maidens lie? etc.

Dame, what makes your ducks to die? etc.

Their wings are cut, and they cannot fly, etc.

261

I saw three ships go sailing by,
  On Christmas Day, on Christmas Day,
I saw three ships go sailing by
  On Christmas Day in the morning.

And what was in those ships all three? etc.

Our Saviour Christ and His Lady, etc.

Pray, whither sailed those ships all three? etc.

O, they sailed into Bethlehem, etc.

And all the bells on earth shall ring, etc.

Then let us all rejoice and sing
  On Christmas Day, on Christmas Day,
Then let us all rejoice and sing
  On Christmas Day in the morning.

262

A nursery form of the Christmas carol above

I saw a ship a-sailing,
  A-sailing on the sea,
And oh, it was laden
  With pretty things for thee (me).

There were comfits in the cabin,
  And apples in the hold;
The sails were made of silk,
  And the masts were made of gold.

Four-and-twenty sailors,
  That sat upon the deck,
Were four-and-twenty white mice
  With chains about their necks.

The captain was a duck,
  With a packet on his back;
And when the ship began to move
  The captain cried, 'Quack! quack!'

Another version runs

> I saw three ships come sailing by, etc.
>> On New Year's Day in the morning.
>
> And what do you think was in them then? etc.
>
> Three pretty girls were in them then, etc.
>
> One could whistle, and one could sing,
>> The other could play on the violin;
> Such joy was there at my wedding,
>> On New Year's Day in the morning.

263

> When Yule comes, dule comes,
>> Cauld feet and legs;
> When Pasch comes, grace comes,
>> Butter, milk, and eggs.

264

> Yule, Yule, Yule,
>> Three puddings in a pule!
> Crack nuts and cry Yule!

265

> Get up, guidwife, and shake your feathers,
> And dinna think that we are beggars,
> We're only bairnies come to play,
> Get up and gie us our Hogmanay.

266

> Blinkin' Jock, the cobbler,
>> He had a blinkin' ee;
> He selt his wife for a hunner pund,
> And that was a' his gear.
> His pockets fu' o' money,
> His barrels fu' o' beer;
> Please tae help the Guisers
> An' we wish ye a happy New Year.

267

A rhyme to be sung in orchards at the New Year

Here stands a good apple-tree;
Stand fast at root,
Bear well at top;
Every little twig
Bear an apple big;
Every little bough
Bear an apple now;
Hats full! Caps full!
Three-score sacks full!
Hullo, boys! hullo!

268

A song for Twelfth Night

Lavender's blue, dilly, dilly, lavender's green,
When I am king, dilly, dilly, you shall be queen;
Call up your men, dilly, dilly, set them to work,
Some to the plough, dilly, dilly, some to the cart;
Some to make hay, dilly, dilly, some to thrash corn;
Whilst you and I, dilly, dilly, keep ourselves warm.

269

First comes Candlemas, and then the new moon,
The next Tuesday after is Fastern's e'en.

A longer version of this given by A. B. Simpson in the *Scottish Educational Journal* for March 22, 1940, runs:

First comes Candlemas an' syne the new mune,
The first Tuesday efter that's aye Fastern's E'en.
That mune oot an' the neist mune's nicht,
The first Sunday efter that's aye Paice richt.

270

If Candlemas-day be dry and fair,
The half o' winter's to come and mair;
If Candlemas-day be wet and foul,
The half o' winter's gane at Yule.

271

On your farm at Candlemas Day
Should be half the straw and two-thirds the hay.

272

Good-morrow to you, Valentine!
Curl your locks as I do mine;
Two before and three behind;
Good-morrow to you, Valentine!

273

The first of April, some do say,
Is set apart for All Fools' Day,
But why the people call it so
Nor I, nor they themselves do know.

See also p. 73, No. 213.

274

Hot-cross Buns! Hot-cross Buns!
One a penny, two a penny,
Hot-cross Buns!

Hot-cross Buns! Hot-cross Buns!
If ye have no daughters
Give them to your sons.

275

Rain on Good Friday and wet Easter Day,
Plenty of grass but little good hay.

276

Good morning, mistress and master,
I wish you a happy day;
Please to smell my garland,
Because it's the first of May.

277

Here we come a-piping,
In Springtime and in May;
Green fruit a-ripening,
And winter fled away.
The queen she sits upon the strand,
Fair as a lily, white as a wand;
Seven billows on the sea,
Horses riding fast and free,
And bells beyond the sand.

This is one of several rhymes for the game of 'Queen Anne', another of which runs as follows

Lady Queen Anne, she sits in her stand,
And a pair of green gloves upon her hand,
As white as a lily, as fair as a swan,
The fairest lady in a' the land;
Come smell my lily, come smell my rose,
Which of my maidens do you choose?
I choose you one, and I choose you all,
And I pray, Miss (. . .) yield up the ball.
The ball is mine and none of yours,
Go to the woods and gather flowers.
Cats and kittens bide within
But we young ladies walk out and in.

or

Queen Anne, Queen Anne, you sit in the sun,
As fair as a lily, as white as a wand,
I send you three letters, and pray read one.
You must read one, if you can't read all,
So pray, Miss (*or* Master) throw up the ball.

The players are divided into two sides which take turns in saying the words of the rhyme. The side containing the Queen remains standing or sitting while the other side advances and retires as it sings. The latter line gives one of their number a ball or some small object to hold in the hand in such a manner that it cannot be perceived, and all the players in this assume the same position for their hands, e.g. behind their backs or arms folded. The Queen has to guess who is holding the ball. If she guesses correctly, the lines change sides. If she guesses incorrectly, the other side reply with 'The ball is mine and none of yours', etc. The ball is then taken by another player on the same side, and so on until the Queen guesses the holder.

278

The fair, fair maid, on the first of May,
That goes to the fields at break of day,
And washes in dew by the whitethorn tree,
Will ever blithe and bonnie be.

279

St. Swithin's Day, if thou dost rain,
For forty days it will remain;
St. Swithin's Day, if thou be fair,
For forty days 't will rain na mair.

280

I bought a beard at Lammas fair;
It's a' awa' but ae hair—
Wag, beardie, wag!

A straw is held between upper lip and chin while this rhyme is
spoken. He who repeats this oftenest without dropping the straw
is held to have won the game.

281

Lammas, Lammas,
At eleven oors,
Fareweel summer
And a' the flooers.

282

The Michaelmas moon
Rises nine nights alike soon.

283

Hallowe'en, ae nicht at e'en,
I heard an unco squeaking;
Doleful Dumps has gotten a wife,
They ca' her Jenny Aiken.

284

Haly on a cabbage-stock; Haly on a bean,
Haly on a cabbage-stock, the morn's Hallowe'en.

G

285

Hey-how for Hallowe'en,
A' the witches to be seen;
Some black, and some green,
Hey-how for Hallowe'en.

286

Remember, remember,
The fifth of November
Gunpowder Treason and Plot.
I see no reason
Why Gunpowder Treason
Should ever be forgot.

287

'Tween Martinmas and Yule
Water's wine in every pool.

288

Truan, truan, trottibus,
Leaves the school at Martinmas,
Comes again at Whitsunday,
When a' the lave get the play.

VOCABULARY OF NUMBER

ONE

289

Rhyme for the game of Conkers, played with horse-chestnuts threaded on string

> Cobbly co!
> My first blow!
> Put down your black hat,
> And let me have first smack!

A winning conker, one which breaks its opponent without being broken, adds its opponent's battle honours to its own. Thus a conker which has overcome five others at their first appearance in play is a fiver. If it triumphs over a sixth which has, say, three to its credit, it becomes an eighter.

290

> Here am I,
> Little jumping Joan,
> When nobody's with me,
> I'm all alone.

See also: 'I had a little sister' (p. 42, No. 109).

291

> Lady-bird, lady-bird, fly away home,
> Thy house is on fire, thy children all gone.
> All but one, that lies under a stone,
> Fly thee home, lady-bird, ere it be gone.

Two

292

Hoolie, the bed'll fa'!
Wha'll fa' wi't?
Twa een, twa hands,
And twa bonnie feet.

Hoolie, the bed'll no fa'!
Wha'll no fa' wi't?
Wee Robin Reidbreist,
Soond asleep.

293

Ma love's ane,
The hiccup's twa;
Gin ma love likes me,
The hiccup'll gang awa.

294

The brown bull o' Baverton
Went o'er the hill to Haverton,
And dashed its head between two stones,
And was brought milk white home.

Answer: Corn sent to the mill.

295

The first time that I gaed to Coudingham fair,
I there fell in with a jolly beggare;
The beggar's name, O, it was Harry,
And he had a wife and they ca'ed her Mary;
O Mary and Harry, and Harry and Mary,
And Janet and John;
That's the beggars one by one;
But now I will gie you them pair by pair,
All the brave beggars of Coudingham fair.

The next time that I went to Coudingham fair,
There I met with another beggare;
The beggar's name, O, it was Willie,
And he had a wife, and they ca'ed her Lillie;
And Harry and Mary, and Willie and Lillie,
And Janet and John;
That's the beggars one by one;
Now I will gie you them pair by pair,
All the brave beggars of Coudingham fair.

The next time . . . etc.
The beggar's name, O, it was Wilkin,
And he had a wife, and they ca'ed her Gilkin;
And Harry and Mary, and Willie and Lillie,
And Wilkin and Gilkin, and Janet and John;
That's the beggars all one by one;
Now . . . etc.

296

They were two jolly fishermen,
They were two jolly fishermen,
They were two jolly fishermen,
   And just come from the sea,
   And just come from the sea.
They cast their nets into the sea,
   And jolly fish caught we,
   And jolly fish caught we,
   And jolly fish caught we,
They cast their nets into the sea,
   And jolly fish caught we.

Sometimes this is played as 'Three Jolly Fishermen'. The players join hands in a circle enclosing two (or three) players, and walk round singing. At the seventh line each of the players in the centre chooses one from the ring, and then sing the remaining lines. At the end, the first two go out and the second two begin the game again.

297

Trip and go, heave and ho,
Up and down, to and fro;
From the town to the grove,
Two and two let us rove;
A-maying, a-playing,
Love hath no gainsaying;
So merrily trip and go,
So merrily trip and go.

298

Turvey, turvey, clothed in black,
With silver buttons upon your back;
One by one, and two by two,
Turn about, and that will do.

The players march two and two in a measured step to a given
distance, then turn and march back again

299

Two little dogs sat by the fire,
Over a fender of coal dust;
When one said to the other dog,
'If Pompey won't talk, why I must.'

THREE

300

Betty Pringle had a little pig,
Not too little and not too big.
When he was alive he lived in clover,
But now he's dead and that's all over.
So Billy Pringle he lay down and cried,
And Betty Pringle she lay down and died.
So there was the end of one, two and three.
       Billy Pringle he
       Betty Pringle she
       And the piggy wiggy.

301

The rhyme for 'Blind Man's Buff'

> Blind man, blind man,
>   Sure you can't see?
> Turn round three times,
>   And try to catch me.
> Turn east, turn west,
>   Catch as you can,
> Did you think you'd caught me?
> Blind, blind man!

302

> How many fingers do I hold up?

> (*Answer at random*)

> How many horses has your father?
> Three.
> What colour?
> White, red and grey.
> Turn you about three times:
> Catch whom you may.

The above, among others, is the introductory rhyme to "Blind Man's Buff" to ensure that the blindfolding is complete

303

A game of pretended thumps

> Bontin's man
> To the town ran:
> He coffed and sold,
> And penny down told:
> The kirk was ane, and the quier was twa,
> And a great muckle thump doun aboon a';
> Doun aboon a', doun aboon a'.

304

Bung the Bucket,
One, two, three,
Off, off, off!

or

Jump a little nag-tail,
One, two, three.

The rhyme for a form of 'Leapfrog' in which the Frogs arrange
themselves in a chain, the first supporting himself against some
solid object and the others upon the one in front. The first Leaper
has to land as far up the row as possible, and the others follow close.
The idea is that the Frogs, or Buckets, should resist their weight.
If they break down under it, the Leapers, or Bungs, take their place.

305

The cat's song

Dirdum drum,
Three threads and a thrum,
Thrum gray, thrum gray!

306

Gantin' bodes wantin'
Ae thing o' three;
Sleep, meat, makin' o'—
Whilk want ye?

307

Here are three men from Botany Bay.
Got any work to give us to-day?
What can you do?
Anything.
Set to work then.

This is an introductory rhyme to a game in which three players
act in dumb show the work of the trade which they have agreed
among themselves to represent. It is the task of the others to
guess the trade.

308

Here come three dukes a-riding,
   A-riding, a-riding;
Here come three dukes a-riding,
   With a rancy, tancy, tay!

What is your good will, sirs? etc.

Our good will is to marry, etc.

Marry one of us, sirs, etc.

You're all too black and greasy, etc.

We're good enough for you, sirs, etc.

You're all as stiff as pokers, etc.

We can bend as much as you, sirs, etc.

Through the kitchen and down the hall,
   I choose the fairest of you all;
The fairest one that I can see
   Is pretty Miss ——, walk with me.

Three players represent dukes, the remainder maidens. The dukes
face the maidens, both sides holding hands, and each side advances
to the other as it sings its own verse, with emphasis on the expression of the appropriate emotion. When a girl is named she crosses
over and joins hands with the dukes. The game then continues with
'four dukes a-riding'.

cf. 'We are three brethren come from Spain' (p. 100, No. 325).

309

Here come three sailors, three by three,
To court your daughter, a fair lady;
Can we have a lodging here, here, here?
Can we have a lodging here?

Sleep, sleep, daughter, do not wake,
Here are three sailors we can't take;
You cannot have a lodging here, here, here,
You cannot have a lodging here.

(*The same formula and response for three soldiers and the same formula for three kings to which the response is*)

Wake, wake, daughter, do not sleep,
Here come three kings that we can take.
You can have a lodging here, here, here,
You can have a lodging here.

Here's my daughter, safe and sound,
And in her pocket one hundred pound,
And on her finger a gay gold ring,
And she is fit to walk with a king.

Here's your daughter, not safe nor sound,
Nor in her pocket one hundred pound,
On her finger no gay gold ring,
I'm sure she's not fit to walk with a king.

The players form into two lines, one representing suitors, the other a mother and daughters. The mother stands a little in advance of her daughters, and this side remains stationary while the suitors advance and retire while singing their verses. The mother sings for her side, turning to address her daughters and back again to reply to the suitors. When she accepts the kings she brings one of her daughters forward and shows the suitors the money in her pocket and the ring on her finger. The daughter goes with the kings who lead her away and pretend to rob her. They then bring her back to her mother singing the last verse, then running off in all directions. The mother and daughters pursue and catch them and they then change sides.

310

Hickup, snicup,
Rise up, right up!
Three drops in the cup
Are good for the hiccup.

311

Roses up and roses down,
Roses in the garden;
I wadna gie ye a bunch o' flowers
For tenpence ha'penny farden.
Take her by the lily-white hand,
Lead her across the water,
Gie her a kiss, and one, two, three,
For she's a lady's daughter.

312

Rosy apple, lemon or pear,
Bunch of roses she shall wear;
Gold and silver by her side,
I know who will be the bride.
Take her by the lily-white hand,
Lead her to the altar,
Give her kisses one, two, three,
Mother's runaway daughter.

The players stand in a circle or a row with one child in the middle
or in front who chooses a partner at the appropriate line. After the
partners have kissed the first retires, and the second takes up the
performance.

313

Round about the punch bowl,—
One, two, three;
If anybody wants a bonnie lassie,
Just take me.

or

The fillan o' the punch bowl,
That wearies me;
The fillan o't up, an' the drinkan o't doun,
An' the kissan o' a bonnie lassie
That cheeries me.

The rhyme for a circle game played by girls. At the end of the
verse the players jump, and if one falls she has to leave the ring.
It continues until all the players fall.

Another form of the verse is

> Round about the punchbowl,
>   Punchbowl, punchbowl,
> Round about the punchbowl, one, two, three.

First time, never to fall, etc.

Second time, the catching time, etc.

Third time, the kissing time, etc.

314

> Rub-a-dub-dub,
> Three men in a tub,
> The butcher, the baker,
> The candlestick-maker.

cf.

> Rub-a-dub-dub,
> Three men in a tub,
> And who do you think they be?
> The butcher, the baker,
> The candlestick-maker,
> Turn 'em out knaves all three.

315

> Tak ane gin ye're thirsty,
> Twa gin ye're hungry,
> But three's fair stealin.

316

> Tammy Tammy Titmoose,
> Lay an egg in ilka hoose,
> Ane for you, and ane for me,
> And ane for Tammy Titmoose.

317

> There was a girl in our town,
> Silk an' satin was her gown,
> Silk an' satin, gold an' velvet,
> Guess her name—three times I've telled it.

Answer: Ann.

318

The wind, the wind, the wind blows high,
The rain comes sparkling from the sky,
(———) says she'll die
For a lad with a rolling eye.
She is handsome, she is pretty,
She is the flower of the golden city.
She's got lovers one, two, three.
Come, pray, and tell me who they be.
(———) says he'll have her,
Someone else is waiting for her.
Lash the whip and away.

319

Three blind mice, see how they run!
They all ran after the farmer's wife,
Who cut off their tails with the carving-knife;
Did you ever hear such a thing in your life
     As three blind mice?

320

Three cats in a wunnock sat,
And every cat had aside her twa;
How mony cats, noo, tae a cat
On that wunnuck sat and nyurd awa?

321

To keep the baby quiet

    Three straws on a staff
    Would make a baby cry and laugh.

322

Three times around went our gallant, gallant ship,
And three times around went she;
Three times around went our gallant, gallant ship,
Then sank to the bottom of the sea.

Children join hands in a circle which goes round three times. At
the fourth line all the players sink to the ground.

323

Three wise men of Gotham
Went to sea in a bowl;
If the bowl had been stronger,
My song would have been longer.

324

Through the needle-e'e, boys,
One, two, three, boys!

This is one of several rhymes for 'Threading the Needle', in which the children stand in pairs in long rows, the last pair holding up their arms in an arch. The children then run through the arch and the new last pair continues. This appears to be a Shrove-tide custom. In other forms the children pass through the needle's eye while holding on to the child in front.

325

We are three brethren come from Spain,
    All in French garlands:
We are come to court your daughter, Jean,
    And adieu to you, my darlings.

My daughter Jean she is too young,
    All in French garlands;
She cannot bide your flattering tongue,
    And adieu to you, my darlings.

Be she young, or be she old,
    All in French garlands;
It's for a bride she must be sold,
    And adieu to you, my darlings.

A bride, a bride, she shall not be,
    All in French garlands;
Till she go through this world with me,
    And adieu to you, my darlings.

Come back, come back, you courteous knights,
    All in French garlands;
Clean up your spurs and make them bright,
    And adieu to you, my darlings.

Smell my lilies, smell my roses,
   All in French garlands;
Which of my maidens do you choose?
   And adieu to you, my darlings.

Are all your daughters safe and sound,
   All in French garlands?
Are all your daughters safe and sound?
   And adieu to you, my darlings.

In every pocket a thousand pounds,
   All in French garlands;
On every finger a gay, gold ring,
   And adieu to you, my darlings.

cf. 'Here come three dukes a-riding' (p. 95, No. 308).

326

Your plack and my plack,
Your plack and my plack,
Your plack and my plack,
   And Jennie's bawbee.

We'll pit them i' the pint stoup,
Pint stoup, pint stoup;
We'll pit them i' the pint stoup,
   And join a' three.

FOUR

327

I'm in every one's way,
   But no one I stop;
My four horns every day
In every way play
And my head is nailed on at the top.

Answer: A turnstile.

328

Red within and red without,
Four corners round about.

Answer: A brick.

329

Round about the rosebush,
Three steps,
Four steps;
All the little boys and girls
Are sitting
On the doorsteps.

330

'Will ye go to the wood?' quo Fozie Mozie;
'Will ye go to the wood?' quo Johnnie Rednosie;
'Will ye go to the wood?' quo Foslin 'ene;
'Will ye go to the wood?' quo brither and kin.

'What to do there?' quo Fozie Mozie; etc.

'To slay the wren,' quo Fozie Mozie; etc.

'What way will ye get her hame?' quo Fozie Mozie; etc.

'We'll hire carts and horse,' quo Fozie Mozie; etc.

'What way will ye get her in?' quo Fozie Mozie; etc.

'We'll drive down the door-checks,' quo Fozie Mozie;

'I'll hae a wing,' quo Fozie Mozie;

'I'll hae anither,' quo Johnnie Rednosie;

'I'll hae a leg,' quo Foslin 'ene;

'And I'll hae anither,' quo brother and kin.

This refers to the carrying about of a wren, tied to the branch of
a tree, on St. Stephen's Day.

SEVEN

331

As I was going to St. Ives,
I met a man with seven wives,
Every wife had seven sacks,
Every sack had seven cats,
Every cat had seven kits:
Kits, cats, sacks and wives,
How many were there going to St. Ives?

332

Seven mile sank, and seven mile fell;
Seven mile's stanning yet, and evermair will.

Answer: The Tower of Babel.

NINE

333

Robin-a-Ree, ye'll no dee wi' me,
Tho' I birl ye round a three times three:
O Robin-a-Ree, O Robin-a-Ree,
O dinna let Robin-a-Reerie dee.

A rhyme for the game of 'Preestcat' or 'Jack's alive' or 'Jock Bulong', in which an object afire, such as a peat, a piece of wood or other ember, is passed round those encircling a hearth, each one saying:

'About wi' that, about wi' that,
Keep alive the preest-cat.'

or the rhyme given above. A forfeit was exacted from the player in whose hand the fire expired.

In one version the holder says

Little Nanny Cockerthaw,
What if I should let her fa'?

and the remaining players reply

Nine sticks and nine stones
Shall be laid on thy bare back bones
If thou shouldst let fa'
Little Nanny Cockerthaw.

Another version is

Ringie, ringie, Red Belt, rides wi' the King,
Nae a penny in's purse t' buy a gold ring.
Bow-ow-ow, fat dog art thou?
Tam Tinker's dog. Bow-ow-ow.

See also p. 123, No. 401.
H

TEN

334

Ten little mice sat down to spin,
Pussy passed by, and just looked in:
What are you at, my jolly ten?
We're making coats for gentlemen.
Shall I come in and cut your threads?
No, for, Puss, you'd bite off our heads.

cf.

Three mice went into a hole to spin . . .

Ten jolly mice sat down to spin . . .

Six little mice sat in a barn to spin . . .

335

Tiggy-tiggy-touchwood, my black hen,
She lays eggs for gentlemen,
Sometimes eight and sometimes ten, (nine)
Tiggy-tiggy-touchwood, my black hen.

This is the rhyme for 'Tig' when players are exempt from capture so long as they are touching wood. 'Wood' may require to be defined before the game begins if there is too much wood about. 'The fun consists in the bold ventures of those who tempt Tiggy to run after them, and contrive to touch wood just before he touches them.'

A counting-out variant of this rhyme is

Inky, pinky, my black hen
Lays eggs for gentlemen;
Whiles ane, whiles twa,
Whiles a bonny black craw.

One, two, three,
You are out.

TWELVE

336

A dozen is twelve,
Or four times three.
Half a dozen is six,
As plain as can be.

THIRTEEN

337

Nixie, Dixie, hickory bow,
    Thirteen Dutchmen in a row;
Two corporals hold a piece of twine,
    To help the Dutchmen form a line.

SIXTEEN

338

My name is Queen Mary,
My age is sixteen,
My father's a farmer in yonder green:
He's plenty of money to dress in silk fu' braw,
For there's nae bonnie laddie can tak me awa'.
One morning I rose and I looked in the glass,
Says I to myself, I'm a handsome young lass;
My hands by my sides, and I give a ha, ha,
For there's nae bonnie laddie tae tak me awa'.

The players join hands in a circle with one player in the middle
and dance round singing. At the words 'can tak me awa'' the
player in the middle chooses another one, and the two wheel round.
Then the singing proceeds. At the exclamation 'ha, ha!' the players
suit the action to the words of the line. Or the players stand in a
line with one in front, who chooses another from the line and
swings round with her.

TWENTY-FOUR

339

Barber, barber, shave a pig,
How many hairs will make a wig?
'Four-and-twenty, that's enough.'
Give the barber a pinch of snuff.

340

Four-and-twenty tailors went to kill a snail,
The best man among them durst not touch her tail;
She put out her horns like a little kyloe cow,
Run, tailors, run! or she'll kill you all e'en now.

341

Fower-an'-twenty Hielandmen
Were ridin' on a snail,
When up cam' the hin'maist
An' trampit on her tail.
O the snail shot oot her wee bit horns,
Jist like a hummel coo.
'Hech!' quo' the foremaist, 'we'll a' be stickit noo!'

342

Fower-an'-twenty tailor lads
Were fechtin' wi' a slug,
'Hallo, sirs!' said ane o' them,
'Jist haud him by the lug!'
But the beastie frae his shell cam' oot,
An' shook his fearsome heid.
'Rin, rin, my tailors bold
Or we will a' be deid!'

343

'What are ye for wi' the pot, guidman?
Say what, are ye for wi' the pot?
We dinna like to see ye, guid man,
Sae thrang about this spot.

We dinna like ye ava, guidman,
We dinna like ye ava,
Are ye gaun to grow a gled, guidman?
And our necks draw and thraw?'

'Your minnie, burdies, ye maun lea';
Ten to my nocket I maun hae;
Ten to my e'enshanks, and or I gae lie,
In my wame I'll lay twa dizzen o' ye by.'

'Try't than, try't than, do what ye can,
Maybe ye maun toomer sleep the nicht, guidman!
Try't than, try't than, Gled-wylie frae the heugh,
A'm no sae saft, Gled-wylie, ye'll find me bauld and teugh.'

This is the rhyme for 'Gled-wylie', a form of 'Fox and Goose',
or 'Hen and Chickens'. A player goes apart and makes as if to
prepare a fire and the other players address him in the first two
verses. He replies in the third and is answered in the fourth by the
leader of the others who all cling to the leader in a string. It is the
leader's task to keep Gled-wylie from the brood while he tries to
break the row and bear one away.

HALF

344

Cackle, cackle, Mother Goose!
Have you any feathers loose?
Truly have I, pretty fellow,
Half enough to fill a pillow;
And here are quills, take one or two,
And down to make a bed for you.

345

Rhyme on the yellow-hammer

Half a paddock, half a toad,
Half a yellow yorling;
Drinks a drap o' the deil's bluid
Every May morning.

346

There was an old man
And he had a calf
And that's half,
He took him out of the stall
And put him on the wall
And that's all.

347

Well sown
Is half grown.

COMPARISON OF NUMBERS

348

A donkey walks on four legs,
  I walk on two,
The last donkey I saw
  Was just like you.

349

The dove says, Coo, coo, what shall I do?
I can scarce maintain two.
Pooh, pooh, says the wren, I have got ten,
And keep them all like gentlemen!

cf. the rhyme from Bute

The wee coorie Ann
Can lay twenty-wan,
But the big cooshie doo
Can only lay two.

350

Three score o' Highland kye,
One booly-backit,
One blind of an eye,
A' the rest hawkit.

INDEFINITE QUANTITIES AND COMPARISON OF QUANTITY AND SIZE

351

A mile of Don's worth two of Dee,
Except for salmon, stone and tree.

352

A wee, wee hoose,
Fu', fu' o' meat,
And neither door nor window
To get in to eat.

Answer: An egg.

353

Banks fu', braes fu',
Gather ye a' the day
Ye'll no gather your neives fu'.

Answer: The mist.

cf.

A hill full, a hole full,
Ye cannot catch a bowlful.

Answer: The mist.

354

Blackthorn! Blackthorn!
Buttermilk and barleycorn;
How many geese have you to-day?
As many as you catch and carry away.

One person faces a row of others, and tries to catch as many as he can as the others run past him to the opposite side; the captives then help to catch the others, the last one to be caught becoming Blackthorn for a new game. The introductory lines are spoken alternately by the other players and Blackthorn.

355

Bonny Kitty Brannie, she stands at the wa',
Gie her little, gie her muckle, she licks up a';
Gie her stanes, she'll eat them—but water, she'll dee:
Come tell this bonny riddleum to me.

Answer: The fire.

356

Buck, buck, how many fingers do I hold up?
(——) you say, but (——) it is;
Buck, buck, how many fingers do I hold up?

These are the words for a guessing game in which one player covers his eyes, while another holds up his fingers. If he guesses correctly, he in turn asks the question; if incorrectly, the guesser pays the penalty (usually of the appropriate number of blows) or continues guessing until he hits the right number. If there are several players, they take it in turn to address the Buck.

357

For every evil under the sun
There is a cure or there is none.
If there be one, try and find it;
If there be none, never mind it.

358

Hicky more, hacky more,
Hung at the kitchen door
    All day long.
    Nothing so long,
    Nothing so strong,
As hicky more, hacky more,
Hung at the kitchen door
    All day long.

Answer: Sunshine.

359

Higher than a house,
Higher than a tree,
Oh, whatever can that be?

Answer: A star.

360

Humpty Dumpty sat on a wall.
Humpty Dumpty had a great fall.
All the King's horses and all the King's men
Couldn't put Humpty Dumpty together again.

361

I had a little husband,
    No bigger than my thumb;
I put him in a pint pot,
    And there I bid him drum.

I gave him some garters,
    To garter up his hose,
And a little handkerchief
    To wipe his pretty nose.

cf.

I got a little manikin, I set him on my thoomiken;
I saddled him, I bridled him, and sent him to the tooniken;
I coffed a pair of garters to tie his little hosiken;
I coffed a pocket napkin to dight his little nosiken;
I sent him to the garden to fetch a pund o' sage,
And fand him in the kitchen neuk kissing little Madge.

362

If all the seas were one sea,
What a great sea that would be!
And if all the trees were one tree,
What a great tree that would be!

And if all the axes were one axe
What a great axe that would be!
And if all the men were one man,
What a great man that would be!

And if the great man took the great axe
And cut down the great tree,
And let it fall into the great sea,
What a splish splash that would be.

363

If all the world were paper,
And all the sea were ink;
And all the trees were bread and cheese,
What should we do for drink?

364

If you have plenty be not greedy,
But share it with the poor and needy;
If you have little, take good care
To give the little birds a share.

365

Jack Sprat could eat no fat,
His wife could eat no lean,
And so between the two of them,
They licked the platter clean.
Jack ate all the lean,
Joan ate all the fat,
The bone they picked it clean,
Then gave it to the cat.

366

Little girl, little girl, where have you been?
Gathering roses to give to the Queen.
Little girl, little girl, what gave she you?
She gave me a diamond as big as my shoe.

367

Little Nanny Etticoat,
   In a white petticoat,
   And a red nose;
The longer she stands,
The shorter she grows.

Answer: A candle.

368

Long legs, crooked thighs,
Little head, and no eyes.

Answer: A pair of tongs.

369

Mair haste, less speed,
Said the tailor to the lang threed.

370

Rhyme on the wren

Malisons, malisons, mair than ten,
That harry the Ladye of Heaven's hen.

371

Mony hawes,
Mony snaws.

If there is much blossom on the hawthorn a hard winter will
follow.

372

Mony rains, mony rowans,
Mony rowans, mony yewns.

'Yewns' are light grain.

373

Of a little take a little,
Manners so to do;
Of a little leave a little;
That is manners too.

374

Riddle-me, riddle-me, riddle-me-ree,
Perhaps you can tell me what this riddle may be!
As deep as a house, as round as a cup,
And all the King's horses can't draw it up.

Answer: A well.

cf.

As round as an apple,
As deep as a cup;
All the Queen's horses
Can't draw it up.

375

Says Tweed to Till:
'What gars ye rin sae still?'
Says Till to Tweed:
'Though ye rin wi' speed,
And I rin slaw,
For each man ye droun,
I droun twa!'

376

Some hae meat
And canna eat,
And some wad eat
That want it;
But we hae meat
And we can eat,
And sae the Lord be thankit.

377

The horny-goloch is an awesome beast,
    Soople and scaly;
It has twa horns, an' a hantle o' feet,
    An' a forkie tailie.

378

The old man in the wilderness said to me,
'How many strawberries grow in the sea?'
I answered him as I thought good,
'As many red herrings as grow in the wood.'

379

There was a king and he had three daughters,
And they all lived in a basin of water;
The basin bended,
My story's ended.
If the basin had been stronger
My story would have been longer.

380

There was an old woman who lived in a shoe,
She had so many children she didn't know what to do;
She gave them some broth without any bread;
She whipped them all soundly and put them to bed.

381

The silly bit chicken, gar cast her a pickle,
And she'll grow meikle, and she'll grow meikle;
And she'll grow meikle, and she'll do guid,
And lay an egg to my little brude.

382

Wha saw the Forty-Second?
Wha saw them gang awa'?
Wha saw the Forty-Second
Gaein' tae the Wapenshaw?
Some o' them gat chappit tatties,
Some o' them gat nane ava:
Some o' them gat barley bannocks
Gaein' tae the Wapenshaw.

Wha saw the Forty-Second,
Wha saw them gang awa'?
Wha saw the Forty-Second,
Marchin' doon the Broomielaw?
Some o' them had tartan troosers,
Some o' them had nane ava;
Some o' them had green umbrellas,
Marchin' doon the Broomielaw.

383

What God never sees,
What the King seldom sees,
What we see every day:
Read my riddle, I pray.
Answer: An equal.

384

Willie, Willie Wastell,
I am on your castle,
A' the dogs in the toun
Winna pu' Willie doun.

or

Like Willie, Willie Wastell,
I am in my castel.
A' the dogs in the toun
Dare not ding me doun.

These are rhymes for the game of 'Tom Tiddler's Ground' in which a line is drawn on the ground behind which one player stands. The game is for the other players to attempt to trespass on the enclosed area without being caught. If they are caught they stand out of the game. The last to be caught becomes the defender in turn.

NUMERATION

385

When V and I together meet,
They make the number Six complete.
When I with V doth meet once more,
Then 'tis they Two can make but Four,
And when that V from I is gone,
Alas! Poor I can make but One.

386

X shall stand for playmates ten;
V for five stout stalwart men;
I for one, as I'm alive;
C for hundred, and D for five;
M for a thousand soldiers true;
And all these figures I've told to you.

ADDITION

387

Ane to gnaw, and ane to saw,
And ane to pay the laird witha'.

cf. the English version of how to sow beans

One for the mouse, one for the crow,
One to rot, and one to grow.

388

As I was going o'er misty moor
I spied three cats at a mill-door;
One was white and one was black,
And one was like my granny's cat.
I hopped o'er t'stile and broke my heel,
I flew to Ireland very weel,
Spied an old woman sat by t'fire,
Sewing silk, jinking keys;
Cat's i't' cream-pot up to t'knees,
Hen's i't' hurdle crowing for day
Cock's i't' barn threshing corn,
I ne'er saw the like sin' I was born.

389

Baa, sheepie, baa,
Foo mony hoggies
Hiv ye the day?
A black and a brookit,
A reid and a rookit,
They haena been coontit
For mony a day.

390

Baa baa black sheep, have you any wool?
Yes, sir, yes, sir, three bags full:
One for my master, one for my dame,
And one for the little boy that lives in our lane.

This can be varied to 'nine bags full' with a distribution of three each.

391

Bell-ell-ell!
There's a fat sheep to kill!
A leg for the provost,
Another for the priest,
The bailies and deacons
They'll tak the niest;
And if the fourth leg we cannot sell,
The sheep it maun live, and gae back to the hill!

392

Chick! my naigie,
Chick! my naigie,
How many miles to Aberdaigy?
Eight and eight, and other eight,
Try to win there by candlclight.

393

Deedle, deedle, dumpling, my son John,
He went to bed with his stockings on;
One stocking off, and one stocking on,
Deedle, deedle, dumpling, my son John.

394

'Donald Cooper, carle,' quo' she,
'Can ye gird my coggie?'
'Couthie carline, that I can,
As weel's ony bodie.

There's ane about the mou' o't,
And ane about the body o't,
And ane about the leggen o't,
And that's a girdit coggie.'

The child is treated as the coggie to be mended.

395

Draw a pail of water
For my lady's daughter;
My father's a king, and my mother's a queen,
My two little sisters are dressed in green,
Stamping grass and parsley,
Marigold leaves and daisies.
One rush, two rush,
Prythee, fine lady, come under my bush.

There are many variants but the most general form appears to be that in which two children face each other, holding each other by both hands, and two others likewise join hands across the other two. They see-saw back and forth singing the lines. One child gets within one pair of enclosing arms, and so on until there is a child within each pair of arms (i.e. four in all).

396

Here's a poor widow from Babylon,
With six poor children all alone;
One can bake, and one can brew,
One can shape, and one can sew,
One can sit at the fire and spin,
One can bake a cake for the King;
Come choose you east, come choose you west,
Come choose the one that you love best.

Girls form a ring, singing this song to one in the middle. The girl in the middle chooses one from the ring, singing:

I choose the fairest that I do see,
M. N. ye'll come to me.

The girl chosen enters the ring, which then sings

> Now they're married, I wish them joy,
> Every year a girl or boy;
> Loving each other like sister and brother,
> I pray this couple may kiss together!

The two girls then kiss, and the first returns to the ring while the
second goes through the same performance, and so on.

397

> Hippety hop to the barber's shop
> To get a stick of candy,
> One for you and one for me,
> And one for sister Mandy.

398

> How many miles to Babylon?
> Threescore miles and ten.
> Can I get there by candle-light?—
> Yes, and back again!
> If your heels are nimble and light,
> You may get there by candle-light.

'A string of boys and girls, each holding by the predecessor's
skirts, approach two others, who with joined and elevated hands
form a double arch. After the dialogue, the line passes through,
and the last is caught by a sudden lowering of the arms—if possible.'

399

> I'll tell you a story about Jack-a-Norie
> And now my story's begun.
> I'll tell you another about Jackie's brother
> And now my story is done.

400

I love sixpence, pretty little sixpence,
I love sixpence better than my life;
I spent a penny of it, I spent another,
And took fourpence home to my wife.

Oh, my little fourpence, pretty little fourpence,
I love fourpence better than my life;
I spent a penny of it, I spent another,
And I took twopence home to my wife.

Oh, my little twopence, my pretty little twopence,
I love twopence better than my life;
I spent a penny of it, I spent another,
And I took nothing home to my wife.

Oh, my little nothing, my pretty little nothing,
What will nothing buy for my wife?
I have nothing, I spend nothing,
I love nothing better than my wife.

401

A Glasgow rhyme for the game of 'Preestcat'

Jock Bulong—a hazel waun',
A poker and a key,
A bowl of meal to Glesca,
Anither to Dundee:
Twa sticks, twa stanes,
Shall be laid on thy banes
If that red stick goes oot in thy haun'.

See 'Robin-a-Ree', (p. 103, No. 333).

402

King and Queen of Cantelon,
How many miles to Babylon?
Eight and eight, and other eight.
Will I get there by candle-light?
If your horse be good and your spurs be bright.
How many men have ye?
Mae nor ye daur come and see.

cf. 'Have you any bread and wine?' (p. 26, No. 67).

Two children, remarkable as good runners, and personating the King and Queen of Cantelon, are placed between two *doons* or places of safety, at one of which a flock of other children pitch themselves. The runners then come forward, and this dialogue takes place between them and some member of the company, all of whom are considered as knights. The company then break forth and make for the opposite *doon* with all their might, and avoiding the two runners, who pursue and endeavour to catch as many as possible. On catching any, the runner places his hand upon their heads when they are said to be *taned*, and are set aside. The game is repeated and continued till all are *taned*.

403

Little Betty Blue
Lost her holiday shoe.
What can little Betty do?
Give her another
To match the other,
And then she may walk in two.

404

Matthew, Mark, Luke and John,
Bless the bed that I lie on;
Four corners to my bed,
Four angels at my head,
One to watch, and one to pray,
And two to bear my soul away.

cf.

Matthew, Mark, Luke and John,
Bless the bed that I lie on;
Four posties to my bed,
Six angels are outspread:
Two to bottom, two to head,
One to watch me while I pray,
One to bear my soul away.

or

Four corners to my bed,
Four angels round my head,
One to read and one to write,
Two to guard my bed at night.

or

> One to watch and two to pray,
> One to keep all fears away.

405

> My mistress sent me unto thine,
> Wi' three young flowers baith fair and fine—
> The Pink, the Rose, and the Gillyflower:
> And as they here do stand,
> Whilk will ye sink, whilk will ye swim,
> And whilk bring hame to land?

Two members of a party give the names, the Pink, the Red Rose, and the Gillyflower, privately to three other members of the party, all three girls or all three boys. If girls are selected, the two who know the names approach a boy with this rhyme. He chooses one of the three names with an approving epithet and rejects the other two with some expression of disapproval. The identities of the persons so accepted and rejected are then revealed in the hope of causing confusion to the chooser.

406

> O, do you know the Muffin Man,
> The Muffin Man, the Muffin Man?
> O, do you know the Muffin Man
> Who lives in Drury Lane?

> Yes, I do know the Muffin Man, etc.

> O, two do know the Muffin Man, etc.

> O, do you know the Muffin Man? etc.

> Yes, we do know the Muffin Man, etc.

> O, four do know the Muffin Man, etc.

> (*Ad lib.*)

It is suggested that this game may be played by a circle consisting of an even number of children, one of whom stands in the centre, and, bowing to his partner, sings the first verse. His partner replies, and the two then skip round inside the circle while the other children sing the third verse. The two inside the circle then face two others in the circle and sing, 'Do you know the Muffin Man?' and the game continues till all are playing.

407

Ring a ring o' roses,
A pocketful of posies,
One for me and one for you,
And one for little Moses.
Hasha, hasha, all fall down.

408

Seven sleepers there be—
The bat, the bee, the butterflee,
The cuckoo an' the swallow,
The heather-bleat an' the corncraik,
Sleep in a little holie.

409

A ball-counting game

Stottie ba', hinnie ba', tell to me,
How mony bairns am I to hae?
Ane to live, and ane to dee,
And ane to sit on the nurse's knee!

cf.

Cook a ball, cherry tree,
Good ball, tell me
How many years I shall be
Before my true love I do see?
One and two, and that makes three;
Thankee, good ball, for telling of me.

410

The grey cat's kittled in Charlie's wig,
The grey cat's kittled in Charlie's wig;
There's ane o' them leevin' an' twa o' them deid,
The grey cat's kittled in Charlie's wig.

411

There was an old woman had three sons,
Jerry and James and John:
Jerry was hung, James was drowned,
John was lost and never was found;
And there was an end of her three sons,
Jerry and James and John.

cf.

There was an old woman had three cows—
Rosy and Colin and Dun:
Rosy and Colin were sold at the fair,
And Dun broke her horn in a fit of despair
And there was an end of her three cows—
Rosy and Colin and Dun.

412

Another rhyme for 'Turn the Basket'

Tip, tip, toe, leerie, lo!
Turn the ship and away you go;
A penny to you, and a penny to me,
And a penny to turn the basket.

See also p. 50, Nos. 134 and 135.

SUBTRACTION

413

Elizabeth, Elspeth, Betsy and Bess,
All went out to seek a bird's nest.
They found one with five eggs in;
They each took one and left four in.

414

John Black and Black Tap
Yer yowes are unco fat.

Oot o' three score and seeven
I hae taen eleeven.

Did ye but ken ma name
Ye wad hang me for the same.

415

For choosing, when both hands, one empty, are held behind the back

Neivy, neivy, nick-nack
Which hand will ye tak'?
Oh tak' the richt or tak' the wrang,
And I'll beguile ye if I can.

416

Oh dear! what can the matter be?
Two old women got up in an apple-tree;
One came down,
The other stayed till Saturday.

417

Six little snails lived in a tree,
Johnny threw a big stone
And down came three.

418

Ten green bottles hanging on the wall,
Ten green bottles hanging on the wall,
Ten green bottles hanging on the wall,
And if one green bottle should accidentally fall
There'd be nine green bottles a-hanging on the wall.

Nine green bottles hanging on the wall, etc.

(and so on down to)

One green bottle hanging on the wall
And if that green bottle should accidentally fall,
There'd be no green bottles hanging there at all.

419

Ten little chickadees sitting on a line,
One flew away and then there were nine.

   Refrain: Chickadee, chickadee, happy and gay,
                Chickadee, chickadee, fly away.

Nine little chickadees on the farmer's gate,
One flew away, and then there were eight.

Eight little chickadees looking up toward heaven,
One flew away and then there were seven.

Seven little chickadees gathering up sticks,
One flew away and then there were six.

Six little chickadees learning how to dive,
One flew away and then there were five.

Five little chickadees sitting at the door, etc.

Four little chickadees could not agree, etc.

Three little chickadees looking at you, etc.

Two little chickadees sitting in the sun, etc.

One little chickadee living all alone,
He flew away and then there was none.

  An American version of the better-known 'Ten Little Nigger
Boys'.

420

Ten little nigger boys went out to dine;
One choked his little self, and then there were nine.

Nine little niggers boys sat up very late;
One overslept himself, and then there were eight.

Eight little nigger boys travelling in Devon;
One said he'd stay there, and then there were seven.

Seven little nigger boys chopping up sticks;
One chopped himself in half, and then there were six.

Six little nigger boys playing with a hive;
A bumble-bee stung one, and then there were five.

Five little nigger boys going in for law;
One got in chancery, and then there were four.

Four little nigger boys going out to sea;
A red herring swallowed one, and then there were three.

Three little nigger boys walking in the Zoo;
A big bear hugged one, and then there were two.

Two little nigger boys sitting in the sun;
One got frizzled up, and then there was one.

One little nigger boy living all alone;
He got married, and then there were none.

421

The fiddler and his wife,
The piper and his mother,
Ate three half cakes, three whole cakes,
And three quarters of another.
How much did each get?

The fiddler's wife was the piper's mother so each got one and
three-quarters in all.

422

The minister, the dominie, and Mr Andrew Lang,
Went to the garden where three pears hang;
Each one took a pear—how many pears then?

Answer: Two—all three are one person.

MULTIPLICATION

423

A bag o' malt, a bag o' salt,
Ten tens a hundred.

Two children stand back to back, arms linked, and weigh each
other as they repeat these lines.

Another version is

Weigh butter, weigh cheese,
Weigh a pound of candlegrease.

424

Gilty-galty, four-and-forty,
Two tens make twenty.

This is the introductory verse to a game of hide-and-seek, after
which the speaker counts up to forty with his eyes closed while the
other players hide.

Another version is

One a bin, two a bin, three a bin, four,
Five a bin, six a bin, seven, gie o'er;
A bunch of pins, come prick my shins,
A loaf brown bread, come knock me down,
    I'm coming!

425

There grows a tree in Great Ballon,
On it springs mony a fragrant flower;
There is twelve branches hangs from it,
And two and fifty nests therein;
Every nest has seven birds,
And every bird its sindery name.

APPENDIX I

Sources used as Standard

Apperson, G. L., *English Proverbs and Proverbial Phrases: A Historical Dictionary*. London: J. M. Dent & Sons Ltd., 1929.

Boyce, E. R. and Bartlett, Kathleen, *Number Rhymes and Finger Plays*. London: Sir Isaac Pitman & Sons, 1940.

Chambers, Robert, *Popular Rhymes of Scotland*. Edinburgh: W. & R. Chambers Ltd. Originally published in part 1826, enlarged edition 1870.

Ford, Robert, *Children's Rhymes, Children's Games, Children's Songs, Children's Stories*. Paisley: Alexander Gardner, 1903.

Gomme, A. B., *The Traditional Games of England, Scotland and Ireland* (with Tunes, Singing-Rhymes and Methods of Playing according to the Variants extant and recorded in different parts of the Kingdom). 2 vols. London: David Nutt, 1894.

Lockhart, L., Eldredge, A. C. and Brown, J. C., *Number Helps including Number Games, Number Rimes, Number Songs, Sense-Training Exercises, and Speed and Accuracy Tests*. Chicago: Rand McNally and Company, 1924.

MacBain, J. Murray, *The London Treasury of Nursery Rhymes*. London: University of London Press Ltd., n.d.

Montgomerie, Norah and William, *Scottish Nursery Rhymes*. London: The Hogarth Press, 1946.

Montgomerie, Norah and William, *Sandy Candy*. London: The Hogarth Press, 1948.

Mother Goose's Book of Nursery Rhymes and Songs. London: J. M. Dent & Sons Ltd., revised edition, Everyman's Library, 1931.

APPENDIX II

Studies in Children's Games, Rhymes and Literature

Bett, H., *The Games of Children, their Origin and History*. London: Methuen & Co. Ltd., 1929.

Bolton, Henry C., *The Counting-Out Rhymes of Children*. London: Elliot Stock, 1888.

Daiken, Leslie, *Children's Games throughout the Year*. London: B. T. Batsford Ltd., 1949.

Darton, J. Harvey, *Children's Books in England: Five Centuries of Social Life*. Cambridge University Press, 1932.

Eckenstein, Lina, *Comparative Studies in Nursery Rhymes*. London: Duckworth & Co., Ltd., 1911.

Gomme, A. B., *The Traditional Games of England, Scotland and Ireland* (with Tunes, Singing-Rhymes and Methods of Playing according to the Variants extant and recorded in different parts of the Kingdom), 2 vols. London: David Nutt, 1894.

Opie, Iona and Peter, *I Saw Esau*. London: Williams & Norgate Ltd., 1947.

INDEX OF FIRST LINES

INDEX OF FIRST LINES

PUBLICATIONS OF THE SCOTTISH COUNCIL FOR RESEARCH IN EDUCATION

I SCOTTISH SPINNING SCHOOLS. (With illustrations)
By IRENE F. M. DEAN, F.R.Hist.Soc.   **5/-** net

II EDUCATION IN ANGUS
By J. C. JESSOP, M.A., Ph.D., F.R.Hist.Soc.   **5/-** net

III CURRICULUM FOR PUPILS OF TWELVE TO FIFTEEN YEARS (Advanced Division). (*Out of Print*)
Subject Reports available, each **6d.** net

IV GROUP TEST FOR COLOUR BLINDNESS. (*Out of Print*)
By MARY COLLINS, M.A., B.Ed., Ph.D., and JAMES DREVER, M.A., B.Sc., D.Phil., and lithographed by C. C. PARKINSON
10/6 net

V THE INTELLIGENCE OF SCOTTISH CHILDREN   **5/-** net

VI ACHIEVEMENT TESTS IN THE PRIMARY SCHOOL
By GREGOR MACGREGOR, M.A., B.Sc., F.E.I.S. (*Out of Print*)
5/- net

VII A HISTORY OF SCOTTISH EXPERIMENTS IN RURAL EDUCATION
By JOHN MASON, M.A., Ph.D.   **5/-** net

VIII THE HISTORY OF MATHEMATICAL TEACHING IN SCOTLAND
By DUNCAN K. WILSON, M.A., B.Sc., Ph.D.   **5/-** net

IX THE PROGNOSTIC VALUE OF UNIVERSITY ENTRANCE EXAMINATIONS IN SCOTLAND   **5/-** net

X TESTS OF ABILITY FOR SECONDARY SCHOOL COURSES
By FRANK M. EARLE, M.Ed., D.Sc. (*Out of Print*) **5/-** net

XI CITY AND RURAL SCHOOLS. (*Out of Print*)
By ALEX. S. MOWAT, M.A., B.Ed.   **1/-** net

XII THE STANDARDISATION OF A GRADED WORD READING TEST
By P. E. VERNON, M.A., Ph.D.   **1/-** net
Test cards reprinted from the above:
1. THE GRADED WORD READING TEST.   **3d.** per copy
2. THE BURT (Rearranged) WORD READING TEST.
3d. per copy

XIII STUDIES IN ARITHMETIC, Volume I. (*Out of Print*) **5/-** net

XIV SCOTTISH PRIMARY SCHOOL ORGANISATION   **1/-** net

XV THE INTELLIGENCE OF A REPRESENTATIVE GROUP OF SCOTTISH CHILDREN
By A. M. MACMEEKEN, M.A., B.Ed., Ph.D.   **5/-** net

XVI AN ANALYSIS OF PERFORMANCE TEST SCORES OF A REPRESENTATIVE GROUP OF SCOTTISH CHILDREN
By Sir GODFREY THOMSON, Ph.D., D.Sc., D.C.L., F.E.I.S. (Hon.)   **5/-** net

PUBLICATIONS (*continued*)

Official publishers to the Scottish Council for Research in Education
The University of London Press Ltd.,
Warwick Square, London, E.C. 4